www.EffortlessMath.com

... So Much More Online!

✓ FREE Math lessons

✓ More Math learning books!

✓ Mathematics Worksheets

✓ Online Math Tutors

Need a PDF version of this book?

Please visit www.EffortlessMath.com

STAAR Math Exercise Book for Grade 6

Student Workbook and Two Realistic STAAR Math Tests

By

Reza Nazari & Ava Ross

All inquiries should be addressed to:

info@effortlessMath.com

www.EffortlessMath.com

ISBN-13: 978-1-970036-27-5

ISBN-10: 1-970036-27-3

Published by: Effortless Math Education

www.EffortlessMath.com

Description

Get ready for the STAAR® Math Test with a PERFECT Math Workbook!

STAAR Math Exercise Book for Grade 6, which reflects the 2019 test guidelines and topics, is dedicated to preparing test takers to ace the STAAR Math Test. This STAAR Math workbook's new edition has been updated to replicate questions appearing on the most recent STAAR Math tests. Here is intensive preparation for the STAAR Math test, and a precious learning tool for test takers who need extra practice in math to raise their STAAR math scores. After completing this workbook, you will have solid foundation and adequate practice that is necessary to ace the STAAR Math test. **This workbook is your ticket to score higher on STAAR Math.**

The updated version of this hands-on workbook represents extensive exercises, math problems, sample STAAR questions, and quizzes with answers and detailed solutions to help you hone your math skills, overcome your exam anxiety, and boost your confidence -- and do your best to defeat STAAR exam on test day.

Each of math exercises is answered in the book and we have provided explanation of the answers for the two full-length STAAR Math practice tests as well which will help test takers find their weak areas and raise their scores. This is a unique and perfect practice book to beat the STAAR Math Test.

Separate math chapters offer a complete review of the STAAR Math test, including:

- ✓ Arithmetic and Number Operations
- ✓ Algebra and Functions,
- ✓ Geometry and Measurement
- ✓ Data analysis, Statistics, & Probability
- ✓ ... and also includes **two full-length practice tests!**

The surest way to succeed on STAAR Math Test is with intensive practice in every math topic tested--and that's what you will get in *STAAR Math Exercise Book.* Each chapter of this focused format has a comprehensive review created by Test Prep experts that goes into detail to cover all of the content likely to appear on the STAAR Math test. Not only does this all-inclusive workbook offer everything you will ever need to conquer STAAR Math test, it also contains two full-length and realistic STAAR Math tests that reflect the format and question types on the STAAR to help you check your exam-readiness and identify where you need more practice.

Effortless Math Workbook for the STAAR Test contains many exciting and unique features to help you improve your test scores, including:

- ✓ Content 100% aligned with the 2019 STAAR test
- ✓ Written by STAAR Math tutors and test experts
- ✓ Complete coverage of all STAAR Math concepts and topics which you will be tested
- ✓ Over 2,500 additional STAAR math practice questions in both multiple-choice and grid-in formats with answers grouped by topic, so you can focus on your weak areas
- ✓ Abundant Math skill building exercises to help test-takers approach different question types that might be unfamiliar to them
- ✓ Exercises on different STAAR Math topics such as integers, percent, equations, polynomials, exponents and radicals
- ✓ 2 full-length practice tests (featuring new question types) with detailed answers

This STAAR Math Workbook and other Effortless Math Education books are used by thousands of students each year to help them review core content areas, brush-up in math, discover their strengths and weaknesses, and achieve their best scores on the STAAR test.

Do NOT take the STAAR test without reviewing the Math questions in this workbook!

About the Author

Reza Nazari is the author of more than 100 Math learning books including:
– **Math and Critical Thinking Challenges:** For the Middle and High School Student
– **GED Math in 30 Days**
– **ASVAB Math Workbook 2018 - 2019**
– **Effortless Math Education Workbooks**
– **and many more Mathematics books ...**

Reza is also an experienced Math instructor and a test–prep expert who has been tutoring students since 2008. Reza is the founder of Effortless Math Education, a tutoring company that has helped many students raise their standardized test scores—and attend the colleges of their dreams. Reza provides an individualized custom learning plan and the personalized attention that makes a difference in how students view math.

You can contact Reza via email at:
reza@EffortlessMath.com

Find Reza's professional profile at:
goo.gl/zoC9rJ

Contents

Chapter 1:

Whole Numbers

Topics that you'll practice in this chapter:

✓ Rounding

✓ Whole Number Addition and Subtraction

✓ Whole Number Multiplication and Division

✓ Rounding and Estimates

"If people do not believe that mathematics is simple, it is only because they do not realize how complicated life is." — John von Neumann

Rounding

✎ **Round each number to the nearest ten.**

1) 24   20

2) 98   100

3) 41   40

4) 26   30

5) 11   10

6) 35   40

7) 84   80

8) 70   70

9) 47   50

10) 63   60

11) 79   80

12) 55   60

✎ **Round each number to the nearest hundred.**

13) 185   200

14) 254   300

15) 729   700

16) 109   100

17) 222   200

18) 311   300

19) 287   300

20) 927   900

21) 670   700

22) 563   600

23) 890   900

24) 479   500

✎ **Round each number to the nearest thousand.**

25) 1,252   1,000

26) 1,950   2,000

27) 5,235   5,000

28) 3,567   4,000

29) 8,027   8,000

30) 52,512   53,000

31) 31,422   31,000

32) 12,723   13,000

33) 61,670   62,000

34) 71,290   71,000

35) 50,930   51,000

36) 38,568   39,000

Whole Number Addition and Subtraction

✎ *Find the sum or subtract.*

1) 1,264
   + 856
   _____
   2120

2) 2,689
   − 456
   _____
   2233

3) 1,432
   − 556
   _____
   876

4) 2,820
   + 464
   _____
   3284

5) 2,170
   + 245
   _____
   2415

6) 3,221
   +2,560
   _____
   5781

7) 3,788
   +1,892
   _____
   5680

8) 4,238
   +2,576
   _____
   6814

9) 3,515
   − 1,675
   _____
   1840

10) 5,550
    − 4,120
    _____
    1430

11) 3,357
    + 5,230
    _____
    8587

12) 4,510
    −3,691
    _____
    819

✎ *Find the missing number.*

13) 450 + 840 = 1,290

14) 1,786 − 440 = 1,346

15) 9900 − 2,600 = 7,500

16) 5,600 − 2,780 = 2820

17) 6,890 + 570 = 7,460

18) 3,322 − 1,795 = 527

Whole Number Multiplication and Division

✍ *Calculate each product.*

1)
$$\begin{array}{r} 26 \\ \times\ 12 \\ \hline 52 \\ 260 \\ \hline 312 \end{array}$$

3)
$$\begin{array}{r} 50 \\ \times\ 14 \\ \hline 200 \\ 500 \\ \hline 700 \end{array}$$

5)
$$\begin{array}{r} 150 \\ \times\ 15 \\ \hline 750 \\ 1500 \\ \hline 2250 \end{array}$$

2)
$$\begin{array}{r} 60 \\ \times\ 15 \\ \hline 300 \\ 600 \\ \hline 900 \end{array}$$

4)
$$\begin{array}{r} 46 \\ \times\ 20 \\ \hline 920 \end{array}$$

6)
$$\begin{array}{r} 120 \\ \times\ 11 \\ \hline 120 \\ 1200 \\ \hline 1320 \end{array}$$

✍ *Find the missing quotient.*

7) $240 \div 5 =$ 48

8) $280 \div 4 =$ 70

9) $360 \div 6 =$ 60

10) $500 \div 10 =$ 50

11) $400 \div 8 =$ 50

12) $720 \div 8 =$ 90

13) $1500 \div 3 =$ 500

14) $2400 \div 6 =$ 400

15) $1600 \div 20 =$ 80

16) $3200 \div 40 =$ 80

✍ *Solve each problem.*

17) $240 \div 4 = N$, $N = $ 60

18) $1250 \div 5 = N$, $N =$ 250

19) $N \div 6 = 75$, $N =$ 450

20) $45 \times N = 270$, $N =$ 6

21) $880 \div N = 220$, $N =$ 40

22) $N \times 8 = 504$, $N =$ 63

Rounding and Estimates

✎ **Estimate the sum by rounding each number to the nearest ten.**

1) $14 + 68 = 80$

2) $82 + 12 = 90$

3) $43 + 66 = 110$

4) $47 + 65 = 120$

5) $553 + 232 = 780$

6) $418 + 846 = 1270$

7) $582 + 277 = 860$

8) $2771 + 1651 = 4420$

✎ **Estimate the product by rounding each number to the nearest ten.**

9) $55 \times 62 = 360$

10) $14 \times 27 = 300$

11) $34 \times 66 = 2100$

12) $18 \times 12 = 200$

13) $62 \times 53 = 3000$

14) $41 \times 26 = 1200$

15) $19 \times 33 = 600$

16) $76 \times 45 = 4000$

✎ **Estimate the sum or product by rounding each number to the nearest ten.**

17) $\begin{array}{r} 34 \\ \times\, 26 \\ \hline 900 \end{array}$

18) $\begin{array}{r} 53 \\ \times\, 18 \\ \hline 1000 \end{array}$

19) $\begin{array}{r} 78 \\ +\, 92 \\ \hline 170 \end{array}$

20) $\begin{array}{r} 55 \\ +\, 94 \\ \hline 150 \end{array}$

21) $\begin{array}{r} 73 \\ \times\, 12 \\ \hline 700 \end{array}$

22) $\begin{array}{r} 81 \\ +\, 53 \\ \hline 130 \end{array}$

Answers of Worksheets – Chapter 1

Rounding

1) 20	13) 200	25) 1,000
2) 100	14) 300	26) 2,000
3) 40	15) 700	27) 5,000
4) 30	16) 100	28) 4,000
5) 10	17) 200	29) 8,000
6) 40	18) 300	30) 53,000
7) 80	19) 300	31) 31,000
8) 70	20) 900	32) 13,000
9) 50	21) 700	33) 62,000
10) 60	22) 600	34) 71,000
11) 80	23) 900	35) 51,000
12) 60	24) 500	36) 39,000

Whole Number Addition and Subtraction

1) 2,120	7) 5,680	13) 840
2) 2,233	8) 6,814	14) 440
3) 876	9) 1,840	15) 10,100
4) 3,284	10) 1,430	16) 2,820
5) 2,415	11) 8,587	17) 570
6) 5,781	12) 819	18) 1,527

Whole Number Multiplication and Division

1) 312	9) 60	17) 60
2) 900	10) 50	18) 250
3) 700	11) 50	19) 450
4) 920	12) 90	20) 6
5) 2,250	13) 500	21) 4
6) 1,320	14) 400	22) 63
7) 48	15) 60	
8) 70	16) 80	

Rounding and Estimates

1) 80	9) 3,600	17) 900
2) 90	10) 300	18) 1,000
3) 110	11) 2,100	19) 170
4) 120	12) 200	20) 150
5) 780	13) 3,000	21) 700
6) 1,270	14) 1,200	22) 130
7) 860	15) 600	
8) 4,420	16) 4,000	

Chapter 2:

Fractions and Decimals

Topics that you'll practice in this chapter:

✓ Simplifying Fractions

✓ Adding and Subtracting Fractions

✓ Multiplying and Dividing Fractions

✓ Adding and Subtract Mixed Numbers

✓ Multiplying and Dividing Mixed Numbers

✓ Adding and Subtracting Decimals

✓ Multiplying and Dividing Decimals

✓ Comparing Decimals

✓ Rounding Decimals

✓ Factoring Numbers

✓ Greatest Common Factor

✓ Least Common Multiple

"A Man is like a fraction whose numerator is what he is and whose denominator is what he thinks of himself. The larger the denominator, the smaller the fraction." –Tolstoy

Simplifying Fractions

✎ **Simplify each fraction to its lowest terms.**

1) $\frac{9}{18} = \frac{1}{2}$

2) $\frac{8}{10} = \frac{4}{5}$

3) $\frac{6}{8} = \frac{3}{4}$

4) $\frac{5}{20} = \frac{1}{4}$

5) $\frac{18}{24} = \frac{3}{4}$

6) $\frac{6}{9} = \frac{2}{3}$

7) $\frac{12}{15} = \frac{4}{5}$

8) $\frac{4}{16} = \frac{1}{4}$

9) $\frac{18}{36} = \frac{1}{2}$

10) $\frac{6}{42} = \frac{1}{7}$

11) $\frac{13}{39} = \frac{1}{3}$

12) $\frac{21}{28} = \frac{3}{4}$

13) $\frac{63}{77} = \frac{9}{11}$

14) $\frac{36}{40} = \frac{9}{10}$

15) $\frac{21}{63} = \frac{1}{3}$

16) $\frac{30}{84} = \frac{5}{14}$

17) $\frac{50}{125} = \frac{2}{5}$

18) $\frac{72}{108} = \frac{2}{3}$

19) $\frac{49}{112} = \frac{7}{16}$

20) $\frac{240}{320} = \frac{3}{4}$

21) $\frac{120}{150} = \frac{4}{5}$

Adding and Subtracting Fractions

✑ *Find the sum.*

1) $\frac{1}{3} + \frac{2}{3} =$

2) $\frac{1}{2} + \frac{1}{3} =$

3) $\frac{2}{5} + \frac{1}{2} =$

4) $\frac{3}{7} + \frac{2}{3} =$

5) $\frac{3}{4} + \frac{2}{5} =$

6) $\frac{3}{5} + \frac{1}{5} =$

7) $\frac{5}{9} + \frac{1}{2} =$

8) $\frac{3}{5} + \frac{3}{8} =$

9) $\frac{5}{9} + \frac{3}{7} =$

10) $\frac{5}{11} + \frac{1}{4} =$

11) $\frac{3}{7} + \frac{1}{6} =$

12) $\frac{3}{14} + \frac{3}{4} =$

✑ *Find the difference.*

13) $\frac{1}{2} - \frac{1}{3} =$

14) $\frac{4}{5} - \frac{2}{3} =$

15) $\frac{2}{3} - \frac{1}{6} =$

16) $\frac{3}{5} - \frac{1}{2} =$

17) $\frac{8}{9} - \frac{2}{5} =$

18) $\frac{4}{7} - \frac{1}{9} =$

19) $\frac{2}{5} - \frac{1}{4} =$

20) $\frac{5}{8} - \frac{2}{6} =$

21) $\frac{4}{15} - \frac{1}{10} =$

22) $\frac{7}{20} - \frac{1}{5} =$

23) $\frac{3}{18} - \frac{1}{12} =$

24) $\frac{9}{24} - \frac{3}{16} =$

Multiplying and Dividing Fractions

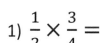 **Find the value of each expression in lowest terms.**

1) $\dfrac{1}{2} \times \dfrac{3}{4} =$ 5) $\dfrac{1}{5} \times \dfrac{1}{4} =$ 9) $\dfrac{8}{9} \times \dfrac{6}{7} =$

2) $\dfrac{3}{5} \times \dfrac{2}{3} =$ 6) $\dfrac{2}{5} \times \dfrac{1}{2} =$ 10) $\dfrac{5}{6} \times \dfrac{3}{5} =$

3) $\dfrac{1}{4} \times \dfrac{2}{5} =$ 7) $\dfrac{7}{9} \times \dfrac{1}{3} =$ 11) $\dfrac{3}{8} \times \dfrac{1}{9} =$

4) $\dfrac{1}{6} \times \dfrac{4}{5} =$ 8) $\dfrac{5}{7} \times \dfrac{3}{8} =$ 12) $\dfrac{1}{12} \times \dfrac{3}{7} =$

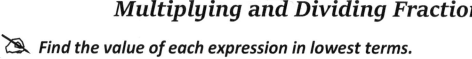 **Find the value of each expression in lowest terms.**

13) $\dfrac{1}{2} \div \dfrac{1}{4} =$ 17) $\dfrac{1}{5} \div \dfrac{3}{10} =$ 21) $\dfrac{4}{13} \div \dfrac{1}{4} =$

14) $\dfrac{1}{3} \div \dfrac{1}{2} =$ 18) $\dfrac{2}{7} \div \dfrac{1}{3} =$ 22) $\dfrac{9}{14} \div \dfrac{3}{7} =$

15) $\dfrac{2}{5} \div \dfrac{1}{3} =$ 19) $\dfrac{3}{5} \div \dfrac{5}{9} =$ 23) $\dfrac{8}{15} \div \dfrac{2}{5} =$

16) $\dfrac{1}{4} \div \dfrac{2}{3} =$ 20) $\dfrac{2}{23} \div \dfrac{2}{9} =$ 24) $\dfrac{2}{9} \div \dfrac{7}{11} =$

Adding and Subtracting Mixed Numbers

✎ **Find the sum.**

1) $2\frac{1}{2} + 1\frac{1}{3} =$

2) $6\frac{1}{2} + 3\frac{1}{2} =$

3) $2\frac{3}{8} + 3\frac{1}{8} =$

4) $4\frac{1}{2} + 1\frac{1}{4} =$

5) $1\frac{3}{7} + 1\frac{5}{14} =$

6) $6\frac{5}{12} + 3\frac{3}{4} =$

7) $5\frac{1}{2} + 8\frac{3}{4} =$

8) $3\frac{7}{8} + 3\frac{1}{3} =$

9) $3\frac{3}{9} + 7\frac{6}{11} =$

10) $7\frac{5}{12} + 4\frac{3}{10} =$

✎ **Find the difference.**

11) $3\frac{1}{3} - 1\frac{1}{3} =$

12) $4\frac{1}{2} - 3\frac{1}{2} =$

13) $5\frac{1}{2} - 2\frac{1}{4} =$

14) $6\frac{1}{6} - 5\frac{1}{3} =$

15) $8\frac{1}{2} - 1\frac{1}{10} =$

16) $9\frac{1}{2} - 2\frac{1}{4} =$

17) $9\frac{1}{5} - 5\frac{1}{6} =$

18) $14\frac{3}{10} - 13\frac{1}{3} =$

19) $19\frac{2}{3} - 11\frac{5}{8} =$

20) $20\frac{3}{4} - 14\frac{2}{3} =$

Multiplying and Dividing Mixed Numbers

✍ *Find the product.*

1) $4\frac{1}{3} \times 2\frac{1}{5} =$

2) $3\frac{1}{2} \times 3\frac{1}{4} =$

3) $5\frac{2}{5} \times 2\frac{1}{3} =$

4) $2\frac{1}{2} \times 1\frac{2}{9} =$

5) $3\frac{4}{7} \times 2\frac{3}{5} =$

6) $7\frac{2}{3} \times 2\frac{2}{3} =$

7) $9\frac{8}{9} \times 8\frac{3}{4} =$

8) $2\frac{4}{7} \times 5\frac{2}{9} =$

9) $5\frac{2}{5} \times 2\frac{3}{5} =$

10) $3\frac{5}{7} \times 3\frac{5}{6} =$

✍ *Find the quotient.*

11) $1\frac{2}{3} \div 3\frac{1}{3} =$

12) $2\frac{1}{4} \div 1\frac{1}{2} =$

13) $10\frac{1}{2} \div 1\frac{2}{3} =$

14) $3\frac{1}{6} \div 4\frac{2}{3} =$

15) $4\frac{1}{8} \div 2\frac{1}{2} =$

16) $2\frac{1}{10} \div 2\frac{3}{5} =$

17) $1\frac{4}{11} \div 1\frac{1}{4} =$

18) $9\frac{1}{2} \div 9\frac{2}{3} =$

19) $8\frac{3}{4} \div 2\frac{2}{5} =$

20) $12\frac{1}{2} \div 9\frac{1}{3} =$

Adding and Subtracting Decimals

✍ **Add and subtract decimals.**

1)
$$\begin{array}{r} 31.13 \\ -\ 11.45 \\ \hline \end{array}$$

4)
$$\begin{array}{r} 56.67 \\ -\ 44.39 \\ \hline \end{array}$$

7)
$$\begin{array}{r} 66.24 \\ -\ 23.11 \\ \hline \end{array}$$

2)
$$\begin{array}{r} 35.25 \\ +\ 24.47 \\ \hline \end{array}$$

5)
$$\begin{array}{r} 71.47 \\ +\ 16.25 \\ \hline \end{array}$$

8)
$$\begin{array}{r} 39.75 \\ +\ 12.85 \\ \hline \end{array}$$

3)
$$\begin{array}{r} 73.50 \\ +\ 22.78 \\ \hline \end{array}$$

6)
$$\begin{array}{r} 68.99 \\ -\ 53.61 \\ \hline \end{array}$$

9)
$$\begin{array}{r} 229.25 \\ -\ 84.67 \\ \hline \end{array}$$

✍ **Find the missing number.**

10) ___ + 2.5 = 3.9

11) 1.7 + ___ = 4.98

12) 5.25 + ___ = 7

13) 6.55 − ___ = 2.45

14) ___ − 3.98 = 5.32

15) ___ − 11.67 = 14.48

16) 12.35 + ___ = 14.78

17) ___ − 23.89 = 13.90

18) ___ + 17.28 = 19.56

19) 77.90 + ___ = 102.60

Multiplying and Dividing Decimals

✎ **Find the product.**

1) $0.5 \times 0.4 =$

2) $2.5 \times 0.2 =$

3) $1.25 \times 0.5 =$

4) $0.75 \times 0.2 =$

5) $1.92 \times 0.8 =$

6) $0.55 \times 0.4 =$

7) $3.24 \times 1.2 =$

8) $12.5 \times 4.2 =$

9) $22.6 \times 8.2 =$

10) $17.2 \times 4.5 =$

11) $25.1 \times 12.5 =$

12) $33.2 \times 2.2 =$

✎ **Find the quotient.**

13) $1.67 \div 100 =$

14) $52.2 \div 1,000 =$

15) $4.2 \div 2 =$

16) $8.6 \div 0.5 =$

17) $12.6 \div 0.2 =$

18) $16.5 \div 5 =$

19) $13.25 \div 100 =$

20) $25.6 \div 0.4 =$

21) $28.24 \div 0.1 =$

22) $34.16 \div 0.25 =$

23) $44.28 \div 0.5 =$

24) $38.78 \div 0.02 =$

Comparing Decimals

✎ *Write the correct comparison symbol (>, < or =).*

1) 0.50 ☐ 0.050

2) 0.025 ☐ 0.25

3) 2.060 ☐ 2.07

4) 1.75 ☐ 1.07

5) 4.04 ☐ 0.440

6) 3.05 ☐ 3.5

7) 5.05 ☐ 5.050

8) 1.02 ☐ 1.1

9) 2.45 ☐ 2.125

10) 0.932 ☐ 0.0932

11) 3.15 ☐ 3.150

12) 0.718 ☐ 0.89

13) 7.060 ☐ 7.60

14) 3.59 ☐ 3.129

15) 4.33 ☐ 4.319

16) 2.25 ☐ 2.250

17) 1.95 ☐ 1.095

18) 8.051 ☐ 8.50

19) 1.022 ☐ 1.020

20) 3.77 ☐ 3.770

Rounding Decimals

✎ **Round each decimal to the nearest whole number.**

1) 23.18	3) 14.45	5) 3.95
2) 8.6	4) 7.5	6) 56.7

✎ **Round each decimal to the nearest tenth.**

7) 22.652	9) 47.847	11) 16.184
8) 30.342	10) 82.88	12) 71.79

✎ **Round each decimal to the nearest hundredth.**

13) 5.439	15) 26.1855	17) 91.448
14) 12.907	16) 48.623	18) 29.354

✎ **Round each decimal to the nearest thousandth.**

19) 14.67374	21) 78.7191	23) 10.0678
20) 7.54647	22) 70.2732	24) 46.54765

Factoring Numbers

✎ *List all positive factors of each number.*

1) 8

2) 9

3) 15

4) 16

5) 25

6) 28

7) 26

8) 35

9) 42

10) 48

11) 50

12) 36

13) 55

14) 40

15) 62

16) 84

17) 75

18) 68

19) 96

20) 78

21) 94

22) 82

23) 81

24) 72

Greatest Common Factor

✍ *Find the GCF for each number pair.*

1) 4, 2   9) 5, 12   17) 32, 24

2) 3, 5   10) 4, 14   18) 18, 36

3) 2, 6   11) 15, 18   19) 26, 20

4) 4, 7   12) 12, 20   20) 30, 14

5) 5, 10   13) 12, 16   21) 24, 20

6) 6, 12   14) 15, 27   22) 14, 22

7) 7, 14   15) 8, 24   23) 25, 15

8) 6, 14   16) 28, 16   24) 28, 32

Least Common Multiple

✎ *Find the LCM for each number pair.*

1) 3, 6

2) 5, 10

3) 6, 14

4) 8, 9

5) 6, 18

6) 10, 12

7) 4, 12

8) 5, 15

9) 4, 18

10) 9, 12

11) 12, 16

12) 15, 18

13) 8, 24

14) 9, 28

15) 12, 24

16) 15, 20

17) 25, 18

18) 27, 24

19) 28, 18

20) 16, 30

21) 14, 28

22) 20, 35

23) 25, 30

24) 32, 27

Answers of Worksheets – Chapter 2

Simplifying Fractions

1) $\frac{1}{2}$

2) $\frac{4}{5}$

3) $\frac{3}{4}$

4) $\frac{1}{4}$

5) $\frac{3}{4}$

6) $\frac{2}{3}$

7) $\frac{4}{5}$

8) $\frac{1}{4}$

9) $\frac{1}{2}$

10) $\frac{1}{7}$

11) $\frac{1}{3}$

12) $\frac{3}{4}$

13) $\frac{9}{11}$

14) $\frac{9}{10}$

15) $\frac{1}{3}$

16) $\frac{5}{14}$

17) $\frac{2}{5}$

18) $\frac{2}{3}$

19) $\frac{7}{16}$

20) $\frac{3}{4}$

21) $\frac{4}{5}$

Adding and Subtracting Fractions

1) $\frac{3}{3} = 1$

2) $\frac{5}{6}$

3) $\frac{9}{10}$

4) $\frac{23}{21}$

5) $\frac{23}{20}$

6) $\frac{4}{5}$

7) $\frac{19}{18}$

8) $\frac{39}{40}$

9) $\frac{62}{63}$

10) $\frac{31}{44}$

11) $\frac{25}{42}$

12) $\frac{27}{28}$

13) $\frac{1}{6}$

14) $\frac{2}{15}$

15) $\frac{1}{2}$

16) $\frac{1}{10}$

17) $\frac{22}{45}$

18) $\frac{29}{63}$

19) $\frac{3}{20}$

20) $\frac{7}{24}$

21) $\frac{1}{6}$

22) $\frac{3}{20}$

23) $\frac{1}{12}$

24) $\frac{3}{16}$

Multiplying and Dividing Fractions

1) $\frac{3}{8}$

2) $\frac{2}{5}$

3) $\frac{1}{10}$

4) $\frac{2}{15}$

5) $\frac{1}{20}$

6) $\frac{1}{5}$

7) $\frac{7}{27}$

8) $\frac{15}{56}$

9) $\frac{16}{21}$

10) $\frac{1}{2}$

11) $\frac{1}{24}$

12) $\frac{1}{28}$

13) 2

14) $\frac{2}{3}$

15) $\frac{6}{5}$

16) $\frac{3}{8}$

17) $\frac{2}{3}$

18) $\frac{6}{7}$

19) $\frac{27}{25}$

20) $\frac{9}{23}$

21) $\frac{16}{13}$

22) $\frac{21}{14}$

23) $\frac{4}{3}$

24) $\frac{22}{63}$

Adding and Subtracting Mixed Numbers

1) $3\frac{5}{6}$

2) 10

3) $5\frac{1}{2}$

4) $5\frac{3}{4}$

5) $2\frac{11}{14}$

6) $10\frac{1}{6}$

7) $14\frac{1}{4}$

8) $7\frac{5}{24}$

9) $10\frac{29}{33}$

10) $11\frac{43}{60}$

11) 2

12) 1

13) $3\frac{1}{4}$

14) $\frac{5}{6}$

15) $7\frac{2}{5}$

16) $7\frac{1}{4}$

17) $4\frac{1}{30}$

18) $\frac{29}{30}$

19) $8\frac{1}{24}$

20) $6\frac{1}{12}$

Multiplying and Dividing Mixed Numbers

1) $9\frac{8}{15}$

2) $11\frac{3}{8}$

3) $12\frac{3}{5}$

4) $3\frac{1}{18}$

5) $9\frac{2}{7}$

6) $20\frac{4}{9}$

7) $86\frac{19}{36}$

8) $13\frac{3}{7}$

9) $14\frac{1}{25}$

10) $14\frac{5}{21}$

11) $\frac{1}{2}$

12) $1\frac{1}{2}$

13) $6\frac{3}{10}$

14) $\frac{19}{28}$

15) $1\frac{13}{20}$

16) $\frac{21}{26}$

17) $1\frac{1}{11}$

18) $\frac{57}{58}$

19) $3\frac{31}{48}$

20) $1\frac{19}{56}$

Adding and Subtracting Decimals

1) 19.68

2) 59.72

3) 96.28

4) 12.28

5) 87.72

6) 15.38

7) 43.13

8) 52.60

9) 144.58

10) 1.4

11) 3.28

12) 1.75

13) 4.1

14) 9.3

15) 26.15

16) 2.43

17) 37.79

18) 2.28

19) 24.7

Multiplying and Dividing Decimals

1) 0.2

2) 0.5

3) 0.625

4) 0.15

5) 1.536

6) 0.22

7) 3.888
8) 52.5
9) 185.32
10) 77.4
11) 313.75
12) 73.04
13) 0.0167

14) 0.0522
15) 2.1
16) 4.3
17) 63
18) 3.3
19) 0.1325
20) 64

21) 282.4
22) 136.64
23) 88.56
24) 1,939

Comparing Decimals

1) >
2) <
3) <
4) >
5) >
6) <
7) =

8) <
9) >
10) >
11) =
12) <
13) <
14) >

15) >
16) =
17) >
18) <
19) >
20) =

Rounding Decimals

1) 23
2) 9
3) 14
4) 8
5) 4
6) 57
7) 22.7
8) 30.3

9) 47.8
10) 82.9
11) 16.2
12) 71.8
13) 5.44
14) 12.91
15) 26.19
16) 48.62

17) 91.45
18) 29.35
19) 14.674
20) 7.546
21) 78.719
22) 70.273
23) 10.068
24) 46.548

Factoring Numbers

1) 1, 2, 4, 8
2) 1, 3, 9
3) 1, 3, 5, 15
4) 1, 2, 4, 8, 16
5) 1, 5, 25
6) 1, 2, 4, 7, 14, 28
7) 1, 2, 13, 26
8) 1, 5, 7, 35
9) 1, 2, 3, 6, 7, 14, 21, 42
10) 1, 2, 3, 4, 6, 8, 12, 16, 24, 48
11) 1, 2, 5, 10, 25, 50
12) 1, 2, 3, 4, 6, 9, 12, 18, 36

13) 1, 5, 11, 55
14) 1, 2, 4, 5, 8, 10, 20, 40
15) 1, 2, 31, 62
16) 1, 2, 3, 4, 6, 7, 12, 14, 21, 28, 42, 84
17) 1, 3, 5, 15, 25, 75
18) 1, 2, 4, 17, 34, 68
19) 1, 2, 3, 4, 6, 8, 12, 16, 24, 32, 48, 96
20) 1, 2, 3, 6, 13, 26, 39, 78
21) 1, 2, 47, 94
22) 1, 2, 41, 82
23) 1, 3, 9, 27, 81
24) 1, 2, 3, 4, 6, 8, 9, 12, 18, 24, 36, 72

Greatest Common Factor

1) 2
2) 1

3) 2
4) 1

5) 5
6) 6

7) 7	13) 4	19) 2
8) 2	14) 3	20) 2
9) 1	15) 8	21) 4
10) 2	16) 4	22) 2
11) 3	17) 8	23) 5
12) 4	18) 18	24) 4

Least Common Multiple

1) 6	9) 36	17) 450
2) 10	10) 36	18) 216
3) 42	11) 48	19) 252
4) 72	12) 90	20) 240
5) 18	13) 24	21) 28
6) 60	14) 252	22) 140
7) 12	15) 24	23) 150
8) 15	16) 60	24) 864

Chapter 3:

Real Numbers and Integers

Topics that you'll practice in this chapter:

✓ Adding and Subtracting Integers

✓ Multiplying and Dividing Integers

✓ Order of Operations

✓ Ordering Integers and Numbers

✓ Integers and Absolute Value

Adding and Subtracting Integers

✍ *Find each sum.*

1) $12 + (-5) =$

2) $(-14) + (-18) =$

3) $8 + (-28) =$

4) $43 + (-12) =$

5) $(-7) + (-11) + 4 =$

6) $37 + (-16) + 12 =$

7) $29 + (-21) + (-12) + 20 =$

8) $(-15) + (-25) + 18 + 25 =$

9) $30 + (-28) + (35 - 32) =$

10) $25 + (-15) + (44 - 17) =$

✍ *Find each difference.*

11) $(-12) - (-8) =$

12) $15 - (-20) =$

13) $(-11) - 25 =$

14) $30 - (-16) =$

15) $56 - (45 - 23) =$

16) $15 - (-4) - (-34) =$

17) $(24 + 14) - (-55) =$

18) $23 - 15 - (-3) =$

19) $49 - (15 + 12) - (-4) =$

20) $29 - (-17) - (-25) =$

Multiplying and Dividing Integers

✍ **Find each product.**

1) $(-7) \times (-8) =$

2) $(-4) \times 5 =$

3) $5 \times (-11) =$

4) $(-5) \times (-20) =$

5) $-(2) \times (-8) \times 3 =$

6) $(12 - 4) \times (-10) =$

7) $14 \times (-10) \times (-5) =$

8) $(18 + 12) \times (-8) =$

9) $9 \times (-15 + 6) \times 3 =$

10) $(-5) \times (-8) \times (-12) =$

✍ **Find each quotient.**

11) $16 \div (-4) =$

12) $(-25) \div (-5) =$

13) $(-40) \div (-8) =$

14) $64 \div (-8) =$

15) $(-49) \div 7 =$

16) $(-112) \div (-4) =$

17) $168 \div (-12) =$

18) $(-121) \div (-11) =$

19) $216 \div (-12) =$

20) $-(152) \div (8) =$

Order of Operations

🖎 *Evaluate each expression.*

1) $5 + (4 \times 2) =$

2) $13 - (2 \times 5) =$

3) $(16 \times 2) + 18 =$

4) $(12 - 5) - (4 \times 3) =$

5) $25 + (14 \div 2) =$

6) $(18 \times 5) \div 5 =$

7) $(48 \div 2) \times (-4) =$

8) $(7 \times 5) + (25 - 12) =$

9) $64 + (3 \times 2) + 8 =$

10) $(20 \times 5) \div (4 + 1) =$

11) $(-9) + (12 \times 6) + 15 =$

12) $(7 \times 8) - (56 \div 4) =$

13) $(4 \times 8 \div 2) - (17 + 11) =$

14) $(18 + 8 - 15) \times 5 - 3 =$

15) $(25 - 12 + 45) \times (95 \div 5) =$

16) $28 + \left(15 - (32 \div 2)\right) =$

17) $(6 + 7 - 4 - 9) + (18 \div 2) =$

18) $(95 - 17) + (10 - 25 + 9) =$

19) $(18 \times 2) + (15 \times 5) - 12 =$

20) $12 + 8 - (42 \times 4) + 50 =$

Ordering Integers and Numbers

 Order each set of integers from least to greatest.

1) $7, -9, -6, -1, 3$ ___, ___, ___, ___, ___, ___

2) $-4, -11, 5, 12, 9$ ___, ___, ___, ___, ___, ___

3) $18, -12, -19, 21, -20$ ___, ___, ___, ___, ___, ___

4) $-15, -25, 18, -7, 32$ ___, ___, ___, ___, ___, ___

5) $37, -42, 28, -11, 34$ ___, ___, ___, ___, ___, ___

6) $78, 46, -19, 77, -24$ ___, ___, ___, ___, ___, ___

 Order each set of integers from greatest to least.

7) $11, 16, -9, -12, -4$ ___, ___, ___, ___, ___, ___

8) $23, 31, -14, -20, 39$ ___, ___, ___, ___, ___, ___

9) $45, -21, -18, 55, -5$ ___, ___, ___, ___, ___, ___

10) $68, 81, -14, -10, 94$ ___, ___, ___, ___, ___, ___

11) $-5, 69, -12, -43, 34$ ___, ___, ___, ___, ___, ___

12) $-56, -25, -30, 18, 29$ ___, ___, ___, ___, ___, ___

Integers and Absolute Value

 Write absolute value of each number.

1) $|-7| =$

2) $|-11| =$

3) $|-9| =$

4) $|8| =$

5) $|4| =$

6) $|-18| =$

7) $|6| =$

8) $|0| =$

9) $|16| =$

10) $|-2| =$

11) $|-12|$

12) $|10| =$

13) $|3| =$

14) $|7| =$

15) $|-15| =$

16) $|-13| =$

17) $|19| =$

18) $|-12| =$

19) $|4| =$

20) $|-25| =$

 Evaluate the value.

21) $|-2| - \dfrac{|-10|}{2} =$

22) $8 - |2 - 14| - |-2| =$

23) $\dfrac{|-36|}{6} \times |-6| =$

24) $\dfrac{|5 \times -3|}{5} \times \dfrac{|-20|}{4} =$

25) $|2 \times -4| + \dfrac{|-40|}{5} =$

26) $\dfrac{|-2|}{4} \times \dfrac{|-55|}{11} =$

27) $|-12 + 4| \times \dfrac{|-4 \times 5|}{2}$

28) $\dfrac{|-10 \times 3|}{2} \times |-12| =$

Answers of Worksheets – Chapter 3

Adding and Subtracting Integers

1) 7
2) −32
3) −20
4) 31
5) −14
6) 33
7) 16

8) 3
9) 5
10) 37
11) −4
12) 35
13) −36
14) 46

15) 34
16) 53
17) 93
18) 11
19) 26
20) 71

Multiplying and Dividing Integers

1) 56
2) −20
3) −55
4) 100
5) 48
6) −80
7) 700

8) −240
9) −243
10) −480
11) −4
12) 5
13) 5
14) −8

15) −7
16) 28
17) −14
18) 11
19) −18
20) −19

Order of Operations

1) 13
2) 3
3) 50
4) −5
5) 32
6) 18
7) −96

8) 48
9) 78
10) 20
11) 78
12) 42
13) −12
14) 52

15) 1,102
16) 27
17) 9
18) 72
19) 99
20) −98

Ordering Integers and Numbers

1) −9, −6, −1, 3, 7
2) −11, −4, 5, 9, 12
3) −20, −19, −12, 18, 21
4) −25, −15, −7, 18, 32
5) −42, −11, 28, 34, 37
6) −24, −19, 46, 77, 78

7) 16, 11, −4, −9, −12
8) 39, 31, 23, −14, −20
9) 55, 45, −5, −18, −21
10) 94, 81, 68, −10, −14
11) 69, 34, −5, −12, −43
12) 29, 18, −25, −30, −56

Integers and Absolute Value

1) 7	11) 12	21) -3
2) 11	12) 10	22) -6
3) 9	13) 3	23) 36
4) 8	14) 7	24) 15
5) 4	15) 15	25) 16
6) 18	16) 13	26) 35
7) 6	17) 19	27) 80
8) 0	18) 12	28) 180
9) 16	19) 4	
10) 2	20) 25	

Chapter 4:

Proportions, Ratios, and Percent

Topics that you'll practice in this chapter:

- ✓ Simplifying Ratios
- ✓ Proportional Ratios
- ✓ Similarity and Ratios
- ✓ Ratio and Rates Word Problems
- ✓ Percentage Calculations
- ✓ Percent Problems
- ✓ Simple Interest

Without mathematics, there's nothing you can do. Everything around you is mathematics. Everything around you is numbers." – Shakuntala Devi

Simplifying Ratios

✎ **Reduce each ratio.**

1) $12:8 =$ ___:___

2) $2:20 =$ ___:___

3) $3:36 =$ ___:___

4) $8:16 =$ ___:___

5) $6:100 =$ ___:___

6) $10:60 =$ ___:___

7) $21:49 =$ ___:___

8) $20:40 =$ ___:___

9) $10:50 =$ ___:___

10) $14:18 =$ ___:___

11) $45:27 =$ ___:___

12) $49:21 =$ ___:___

13) $100:10 =$ ___:___

14) $35:45 =$ ___:___

15) $8:20 =$ ___:___

16) $25:35 =$ ___:___

17) $21:27 =$ ___:___

18) $52:82 =$ ___:___

19) $12:36 =$ ___:___

20) $24:3 =$ ___:___

21) $15:30 =$ ___:___

22) $14:63 =$ ___:___

23) $68:80 =$ ___:___

24) $8:80 =$ ___:___

✎ **Write each ratio as a fraction in simplest form.**

25) $2:4 =$

26) $6:20 =$

27) $5:35 =$

28) $10:55 =$

29) $8:24 =$

30) $9:42 =$

31) $12:48 =$

32) $6:40 =$

33) $15:36 =$

34) $18:82 =$

35) $22:26 =$

36) $8:36 =$

37) $16:128 =$

38) $14:77 =$

39) $12:180 =$

40) $36:108 =$

41) $24:42 =$

42) $18:120 =$

43) $44:82 =$

44) $60:240 =$

45) $36:180 =$

Proportional Ratios

✎ **Fill in the blanks; solve each proportion.**

1) $3 : 7 = \underline{} : 49$

2) $1 : 2 = 20 : \underline{}$

3) $1 : 5 = \underline{} : 50$

4) $7 : 9 = 14 : \underline{}$

5) $5 : 3 = 45 : \underline{}$

6) $7 : 3 = \underline{} : 18$

7) $10 : 1 = \underline{} : 10$

8) $1 : 3 = \underline{} : 27$

9) $8 : 1 = \underline{} : 8$

10) $9 : 2 = \underline{} : 14$

11) $3 : 12 = 12 : \underline{}$

12) $6 : 4 = 24 : \underline{}$

✎ **State if each pair of ratios form a proportion.**

13) $\frac{3}{10}$ and $\frac{9}{30}$

14) $\frac{1}{2}$ and $\frac{16}{32}$

15) $\frac{5}{6}$ and $\frac{35}{42}$

16) $\frac{3}{7}$ and $\frac{27}{72}$

17) $\frac{2}{5}$ and $\frac{16}{45}$

18) $\frac{4}{9}$ and $\frac{40}{81}$

19) $\frac{6}{11}$ and $\frac{42}{77}$

20) $\frac{1}{6}$ and $\frac{8}{48}$

21) $\frac{6}{17}$ and $\frac{36}{85}$

22) $\frac{2}{7}$ and $\frac{24}{86}$

23) $\frac{12}{19}$ and $\frac{156}{247}$

24) $\frac{13}{21}$ and $\frac{182}{294}$

✎ **Solve each proportion.**

25) $\frac{2}{5} = \frac{14}{x}, x = \underline{}$

26) $\frac{1}{6} = \frac{7}{x}, x = \underline{}$

27) $\frac{3}{5} = \frac{27}{x}, x = \underline{}$

28) $\frac{1}{5} = \frac{x}{80}, x = \underline{}$

29) $\frac{3}{7} = \frac{x}{63}, x = \underline{}$

30) $\frac{1}{4} = \frac{13}{x}, x = \underline{}$

31) $\frac{7}{9} = \frac{56}{x}, x = \underline{}$

32) $\frac{6}{11} = \frac{42}{x}, x = \underline{}$

33) $\frac{4}{7} = \frac{x}{77}, x = \underline{}$

34) $\frac{5}{13} = \frac{x}{143}, x = \underline{}$

35) $\frac{7}{19} = \frac{x}{209}, x = \underline{}$

36) $\frac{3}{13} = \frac{x}{195}, x = \underline{}$

Similarity and Ratios

✏️ *Each pair of figures is similar. Find the missing side.*

1)

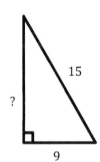

2)

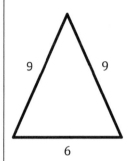

3)

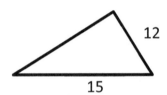

4)

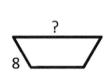
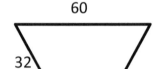

✏️ **Solve.**

5) Two rectangles are similar. The first is 6 feet wide and 20 feet long. The second is 15 feet wide. What is the length of the second rectangle? _____

6) Two rectangles are similar. One is 2.5 meters by 9 meters. The longer side of the second rectangle is 22.5 meters. What is the other side of the second rectangle? _____

7) A building casts a shadow 24 ft long. At the same time a girl 5 ft tall casts a shadow 2 ft long. How tall is the building? _____

8) The scale of a map of Texas is 2 inches: 45 miles. If you measure the distance from Dallas to Martin County as 14.4 inches, approximately how far is Martin County from Dallas? _____

Ratio and Rates Word Problems

✍ *Solve each word problem.*

1) Bob has 12 red cards and 20 green cards. What is the ratio of Bob's red cards to his green cards? _____

2) In a party, 10 soft drinks are required for every 12 guests. If there are 252 guests, how many soft drinks is required? _____

3) In Jack's class, 18 of the students are tall and 10 are short. In Michael's class 54 students are tall and 30 students are short. Which class has a higher ratio of tall to short students? _____

4) The price of 3 apples at the Quick Market is $1.44. The price of 5 of the same apples at Walmart is $2.50. Which place is the better buy? _____

5) The bakers at a Bakery can make 160 bagels in 4 hours. How many bagels can they bake in 16 hours? What is that rate per hour? _____

6) You can buy 5 cans of green beans at a supermarket for $3.40. How much does it cost to buy 35 cans of green beans? _____

7) The ratio of boys to girls in a class is 2:3. If there are 18 boys in the class, how many girls are in that class? _____

8) The ratio of red marbles to blue marbles in a bag is 3:4. If there are 42 marbles in the bag, how many of the marbles are red? _____

Percentage Calculations

✍ **Calculate the given percent of each value.**

1) 2% of 50 = ____

2) 10% of 30 = ____

3) 20% of 25 = ____

4) 50% of 80 = ____

5) 40% of 200 = ____

6) 20% of 45 = ____

7) 35% of 20 = ____

8) 12% of 400 = ____

9) 40% of 90 = ____

10) 25% of 812 = ____

11) 32% of 600 = ____

12) 87% of 500 = ____

13) 77% of 300 = ____

14) 29% of 86 = ____

15) 33% of 54 = ____

16) 71% of 112 = ____

17) 44% of 165 = ____

18) 17% of 232 = ____

✍ **Calculate the percent of each given value.**

19) ____% of 7 = 3.5

20) ____% of 15 = 9

21) ____% of 80 = 4

22) ____% of 50 = 12.5

23) ____% of 64 = 8

24) ____% of 72 = 18

25) ____% of 250 = 12.5

26) ____% of 400 = 12

27) ____% of 190 = 9.5

28) ___% of 900 = 126

✍ **Solve each percent problem.**

29) A Cinema has 240 seats. 144 seats were sold for the current movie. What percent of seats are empty? _____ %

30) There are 18 boys and 46 girls in a class. 87.5% of the students in the class take the bus to school. How many students do not take the bus to school? _____

Percent Problems

✍ **Solve each problem.**

1) 20 is what percent of 50? ____%

2) 18 is what percent of 90? ____%

3) 12 is what percent of 15? ____%

4) 16 is what percent of 200? ____%

5) 24 is what percent of 800? ____%

6) 48 is what percent of 4,00? ____%

7) 90 is what percent of 750? ____%

8) 24 is what percent of 300? ____%

9) 60 is what percent of 400? ____%

10) 42 *is what percent of 350?* ___%

11) 11 *is what percent of 44?* ___%

12) 8 *is what percent of 64?* ___%

13) 210 *is what percent of 875?* ___%

14) 80 *is what percent of 64?* ___%

15) 15 *is what percent of 12?* ___%

16) 56 *is what percent of 40?* ___%

17) 36 *is what percent of 240?* ___%

18) 32 *is what percent of 20?* ___%

✍ **Solve each percent word problem.**

19) There are 48 employees in a company. On a certain day, 36 were present. What percent showed up for work? _____%

20) A metal bar weighs 24 ounces. 15% of the bar is gold. How many ounces of gold are in the bar? _____

21) A crew is made up of 12 women; the rest are men. If 20% of the crew are women, how many people are in the crew? _____

22) There are 48 students in a class and 6 of them are girls. What percent are boys? _____%

23) The Royals softball team played 75 games and won 60 of them. What percent of the games did they lose? _____%

Simple Interest

✍ **Determine the simple interest for these loans.**

1) $450 at 7% for 2 years. $ _____

2) $5,200 at 4% for 3 years. $ _____

3) $1,300 at 5% for 6 years. $ _____

4) $5,400 at 3.5% for 6 months. $ _____

5) $600 at 4% for 9 months. $ _____

6) $24,000 at 5.5% for 5 years. $ _____

7) $15,600 at 3% for 2 years. $ _____

8) $1,200 at 5.5% for 4 years. $ _____

9) $1,600 at 4.5 % for 9 months. $ _____

10) $12,000 at 2.2% for 5 years. $

_____

✍ **Solve each simple interest word problem.**

11)   A new car, valued at $28,000, depreciates at 9% per year. What is the value of the car one year after purchase? $_____

12)   Sara puts $4,000 into an investment yielding 5% annual simple interest; she left the money in for five years. How much interest does Sara get at the end of those five years? $_____

13)   A bank is offering 3.5% simple interest on a savings account. If you deposit $7,500, how much interest will you earn in two years? $_____

14) $400 interest is earned on a principal of $2,000 at a simple interest rate of 5% interest per year. For how many years was the principal invested? _____

15)   In how many years will $1,200 yield an interest of $180 at 3% simple interest? _____

16)   Jim invested $4,000 in a bond at a yearly rate of 4.5%. He earned $540 in interest. How long was the money invested? _____

Answers of Worksheets – Chapter 4

Simplifying Ratios

1) 3 : 2
2) 1 : 10
3) 1 : 12
4) 1 : 2
5) 3 : 50
6) 1 : 6
7) 3 : 7
8) 1 : 2
9) 1 : 5
10) 7 : 9
11) 5 : 3
12) 7 : 3
13) 10 : 1
14) 7 : 9
15) 2 : 5
16) 5 : 7
17) 7 : 9
18) 26 : 41

19) 1 : 3
20) 8 : 1
21) 1 : 2
22) 2 : 9
23) 17 : 20
24) 1 : 10
25) $\frac{1}{2}$
26) $\frac{3}{10}$
27) $\frac{1}{7}$
28) $\frac{2}{11}$
29) $\frac{1}{3}$
30) $\frac{3}{14}$
31) $\frac{1}{4}$
32) $\frac{3}{20}$

33) $\frac{5}{12}$
34) $\frac{9}{41}$
35) $\frac{11}{13}$
36) $\frac{2}{9}$
37) $\frac{1}{8}$
38) $\frac{2}{11}$
39) $\frac{1}{15}$
40) $\frac{1}{3}$
41) $\frac{4}{7}$
42) $\frac{3}{20}$
43) $\frac{22}{41}$
44) $\frac{1}{4}$
45) $\frac{1}{5}$

Proportional Ratios

1) 21
2) 40
3) 10
4) 18
5) 27
6) 42
7) 100
8) 9
9) 64
10) 63
11) 48
12) 16

13) Yes
14) Yes
15) Yes
16) No
17) No
18) No
19) Yes
20) Yes
21) No
22) No
23) Yes
24) Yes

25) 35
26) 42
27) 45
28) 16
29) 27
30) 52
31) 72
32) 77
33) 44
34) 55
35) 77
36) 45

Similarity and ratios

1) 12
2) 2
3) 5
4) 15
5) 50 feet
6) 6.25 meters
7) 60 feet
8) 324 miles

Ratio and Rates Word Problems

1) 3 : 5
2) 210
3) The ratio for both classes is 9 to 5.
4) Quick Market is a better buy.
5) 640, the rate is 40 per hour.
6) $23.80
7) 27
8) 18

Percentage Calculations

1) 1
2) 3
3) 5
4) 40
5) 80
6) 9
7) 7
8) 48
9) 36
10) 203
11) 192
12) 435
13) 231
14) 24.94
15) 17.82
16) 79.52
17) 72.6
18) 39.44
19) 50%
20) 60%
21) 5%
22) 25%
23) 12.5%
24) 25%
25) 5%
26) 3%
27) 5%
28) 14%
29) 40%
30) 8

Percent Problems

1) 40%
2) 20%
3) 80%
4) 8%
5) 3%
6) 12%
7) 12%
8) 8%
9) 15%
10) 12%
11) 25%
12) 12.5%
13) 24%
14) 125%
15) 125%
16) 140%
17) 15%
18) 160%
19) 75%
20) 3.6 ounces
21) 60
22) 87.5%
23) 20%

Simple Interest

1) $63.00
2) $624.00
3) $390.00

4) $94.50

5) $18.00

6) $6,600.00

7) $936.00

8) $264.00

9) $54

10) $1,320.00

11) $25,480.00

12) $1,000.00

13) $525.00

14)   4 years

15)   5 years

16)   3 years

Chapter 5:

Algebraic Expressions

Topics that you'll practice in this chapter:

✓ Translate Phrases into an Algebraic Statement

✓ The Distributive Property

✓ Evaluating One Variable Expressions

✓ Evaluating Two Variables Expressions

✓ Combining like Terms

Mathematics is, as it were, a sensuous logic, and relates to philosophy as do the arts, music, and plastic art to poetry. — K. Shegel

Translate Phrases into an Algebraic Statement

✎ **Write an algebraic expression for each phrase.**

1) 4 multiplied by x. _____

2) Subtract 8 from y. _____

3) 6 divided by x. _____

4) 12 decreased by y. _____

5) Add y to 9. _____

6) The square of 5. _____

7) x raised to the fourth power. _____

8) The sum of nine and a number. _____

9) The difference between sixty–four and y. _____

10) The quotient of twelve and a number. _____

11) The quotient of the square of x and 7. _____

12) The difference between x and 8 is 22. _____

13) 2 times a reduced by the square of b. _____

14) Subtract the product of a and b from 12. _____

The Distributive Property

✏️ **Use the distributive property to simply each expression.**

1) $2(2 + 3x) =$

2) $3(5 + 5x) =$

3) $4(3x - 8) =$

4) $(6x - 2)(-2) =$

5) $(-3)(x + 2) =$

6) $(2 + 2x)5 =$

7) $(-4)(4 - 2x) =$

8) $-(-2 - 5x) =$

9) $(-6x + 2)(-1) =$

10) $(-5)(x - 2) =$

11) $-(7 - 3x) =$

12) $8(8 + 2x) =$

13) $2(12 + 2x) =$

14) $(-6x + 8)4 =$

15) $(3 - 6x)(-7) =$

16) $(-12)(2x + 1) =$

17) $(8 - 2x)9 =$

18) $5(7 + 9x) =$

19) $11(5x + 2) =$

20) $(-4x + 6)6 =$

21) $(3 - 6x)(-8) =$

22) $(-12)(2x - 3) =$

23) $(10 - 2x)9 =$

24) $(-5)(11x - 2) =$

25) $(1 - 9x)(-10) =$

26) $(-6)(x + 8) =$

27) $(-4 + 3x)(-8) =$

28) $(-5)(1 - 11x) =$

29) $11(3x - 12) =$

30) $(-12x + 14)(-5) =$

31) $(-5)(4x - 1) + 4(x + 2) =$

32) $(-3)(x + 4) - (2 + 3x) =$

Evaluating One Variable Expressions

✎ **Evaluate each expression using the value given.**

1) $5 + x$, $x = 2$

2) $x - 2$, $x = 4$

3) $8x + 1$, $x = 9$

4) $x - 12$, $x = -1$

5) $9 - x$, $x = 3$

6) $x + 2$, $x = 5$

7) $3x + 7$, $x = 6$

8) $x + (-5)$, $x = -2$

9) $3x + 6$, $x = 4$

10) $4x + 6$, $x = -1$

11) $10 + 2x - 6$, $x = 3$

12) $10 - 3x$, $x = 8$

13) $2x - 5$, $x = 4$

14) $5x + 6$, $x = -3$

15) $12x + 6$, $x = 2$

16) $10 - 3x$, $x = -2$

17) $5(6x + 2)$, $x = 8$

18) $2(-7x - 2)$, $x = 3$

19) $9x - 3x + 12$, $x = 6$

20) $(6x + 3) \div 5$, $x = 2$

21) $(x + 16) \div 3$, $x = 8$

22) $4x - 12 + 8x$, $x = -6$

23) $(16 - 12x)(-2)$, $x = -3$

24) $12x^2 + 5x - 3$, $x = 2$

25) $x^2 - 11x$, $x = -4$

26) $2x(6 - 4x)$, $x = 5$

27) $14x + 7 - 3x^2$, $x = -3$

28) $(-5)(10x - 20 + 2x)$, $x = 2$

29) $(-3) + \frac{x}{4} + 2x$, $x = 16$

30) $(-2) + \frac{x}{7}$, $x = 21$

31) $\left(-\frac{14}{x}\right) - 9 + 4x$, $x = 2$

32) $\left(-\frac{6}{x}\right) - 9 + 2x$, $x = 3$

Evaluating Two Variables Expressions

 Evaluate each expression using the values given.

1) $2x + 4y$,

   $x = 3, y = 2$

2) $8x + 5y$,

   $x = 1, y = 5$

3) $-2a + 4b$,

   $a = 6, b = 3$

4) $4x + 7 - 2y$,

   $x = 7, y = 6$

5) $5z + 12 - 4k$,

   $z = 5 , k = 2$

6) $2(-x - 2y)$,

   $x = 6, y = 9$

7) $18a + 2b$,

   $a = 2, b = 8$

8) $4x \div 3y$,

   $x = 3, y = 2$

9) $2x + 15 + 4y$,

   $x = -2, y = 4$

10) $4a - (15 - b)$,

   $a = 4, b = 6$

11) $5z + 19 + 8k$,

   $z = -5, k = 4$

12) $xy + 12 + 5x$,

   $x = 7, y = 2$

13) $2x + 4y - 3 + 2$,

   $x = 5, y = 3$

14) $\left(-\frac{12}{x}\right) + 1 + 5y$,

   $x = 6, y = 8$

15) $(-4)(-2a - 2b)$,

   $a = 5, b = 3$

16) $10 + 3x + 7 - 2y$,

   $x = 7, y = 6$

17) $9x + 2 - 4y + 5$,

   $x = 7, y = 5$

18) $6 + 3(-2x - 3y)$,

   $x = 9, y = 7$

19) $2x + 14 + 4y$,

   $x = 6, y = 8$

20) $4a - (5a - b) + 5$,

   $a = 4, b = 6$

Combining like Terms

✎ **Simplify each expression.**

1) $2x + x + 2 =$

2) $2(5x - 3) =$

3) $7x - 2x + 8 =$

4) $(-4)(3x - 5) =$

5) $9x - 7x - 5 =$

6) $16x - 5 + 8x =$

7) $5 - (5x + 6) =$

8) $-12x + 7 - 10x =$

9) $7x - 11 - 2x + 2 =$

10) $12x + 4x - 21 =$

11) $5 + 2x - 8 =$

12) $(-2x + 6)2 =$

13) $7 + 3x + 6x - 4 =$

14) $9(x - 7x) - 5 =$

15) $7(3x + 6) + 2x =$

16) $3x - 12 - 5x =$

17) $2(4 + 3x) - 7x =$

18) $22x + 6 + 2x =$

19) $(-5x) + 12 + 7x =$

20) $(-3x) - 9 + 15x =$

21) $2(5x + 7) + 8x =$

22) $2(9 - 3x) - 17x =$

23) $-4x - (6 - 14x) =$

24) $(-4) - (3)(5x + 8) =$

25) $(-2)(9x - 3) - 12x =$

26) $-22x + 6 + 4x - 3x =$

27) $4(-13x + 2) - 14x =$

28) $-6x - 19 + 15x =$

29) $21x - 12x + 6 - 7x =$

30) $5(6x + 2x) - 15 =$

31) $18 - 12x - 25 - 15x =$

32) $-3(-4x - 2x) + 8x =$

Answers of Worksheets – Chapter 5

Translate Phrases into an Algebraic Statement

1) $4x$
2) $y - 8$
3) $\frac{6}{x}$
4) $12 - y$
5) $y + 9$

6) 5^2
7) x^4
8) $9 + x$
9) $64 - y$
10) $\frac{12}{x}$

11) $\frac{x^2}{7}$
12) $x - 8 = 22$
13) $2a - b^2$
14) $12 - ab$

The Distributive Property

1) $6x + 4$
2) $15x + 15$
3) $12x - 32$
4) $-12x + 4$
5) $-3x - 6$
6) $10x + 10$
7) $8x - 16$
8) $5x + 2$
9) $6x - 2$
10) $-5x + 10$
11) $3x - 7$

12) $16x + 64$
13) $4x + 24$
14) $-24x + 32$
15) $42x - 21$
16) $-24x - 12$
17) $-18x + 72$
18) $45x + 35$
19) $55x + 22$
20) $-24x + 36$
21) $48x - 24$
22) $-24x + 36$

23) $-18x + 90$
24) $-55x + 10$
25) $90x - 10$
26) $-6x - 48$
27) $-24x + 32$
28) $55x - 5$
29) $33x - 132$
30) $60x - 70$
31) $-16x + 13$
32) $-6x - 14$

Evaluating One Variables

1) 7
2) 2
3) 73
4) −13
5) 6
6) 7
7) 25
8) −7
9) 18
10) 2
11) 10

12) −14
13) 3
14) −9
15) 30
16) 16
17) 250
18) −46
19) 48
20) 3
21) 8
22) −84

23) −104
24) 55
25) 60
26) −140
27) −62
28) −20
29) 33
30) 1
31) −8
32) −5

Evaluating Two Variables

1) 14
2) 33
3) 0

4) 23
5) 29
6) −48

7) 52
8) 2
9) 27

10) 7

11) 26

12) 61

13) 21

14) 39

15) 64

16) 26

17) 50

18) −111

19) 58

20) 7

Combining like Terms

1) $3x + 2$

2) $10x - 6$

3) $5x + 8$

4) $-12x + 20$

5) $2x - 5$

6) $24x - 5$

7) $-5x - 1$

8) $-22x + 7$

9) $5x - 9$

10) $16x - 21$

11) $2x - 3$

12) $-4x + 12$

13) $9x + 3$

14) $-54x - 5$

15) $23x + 42$

16) $-2x - 12$

17) $-x + 8$

18) $24x + 6$

19) $2x + 12$

20) $12x - 9$

21) $18x + 14$

22) $-23x + 18$

23) $10x - 6$

24) $-15x - 28$

25) $-30x + 6$

26) $-21x + 6$

27) $-66x + 8$

28) $9x - 19$

29) $2x + 6$

30) $40x - 15$

31) $-27x - 7$

32) $26x$

Chapter 6:

Equations and Inequalities

Topics that you'll practice in this chapter:

✓ Equations

✓ Graphing Inequalities

✓ One–Step Inequalities

Equations

✎ **Solve each equation.**

1) $2x = 20, x =$ ____

2) $4x = 16, x =$ ____

3) $8x = 24, x =$ ____

4) $6x = 30, x =$ ____

5) $x + 5 = 8, x =$ ____

6) $x - 1 = 5, x =$ ____

7) $x - 8 = 3, x =$ ____

8) $x + 6 = 12, x =$ ____

9) $x - 2 = 17, x =$ ____

10) $8 = 12 + x, x =$ ____

11) $x - 5 = 4, x =$ ____

12) $2 - x = -12, x =$ ____

13) $16 = -4 + x, x =$ ____

14) $x - 4 = -25, x =$ ____

15) $x + 12 = -9, x =$ ____

16) $14 = 18 - x, x =$ ____

17) $2 + x = -14, x =$ ____

18) $x - 5 = 15, x =$ ____

19) $25 = x - 5, x =$ ____

20) $x - 3 = -12, x =$ ____

21) $x - 12 = 12, x =$ ____

22) $x - 12 = -25, x =$ ____

23) $x - 13 = 32, x =$ ____

24) $-55 = x - 18, x =$ ____

25) $x - 12 = 18, x =$ ____

26) $5 = 4x - 11, x =$ ____

27) $x - 30 = 20, x =$ ____

28) $x - 12 = 32, x =$ ____

29) $36 - x = 3, x =$ ____

30) $x - 14 = 14, x =$ ____

Graphing Inequalities

 Draw a graph for each inequality.

1) $x > 2$

2) $x < 5$

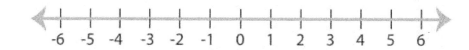

3) $x > -1$

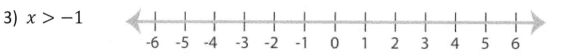

4) $x > 3$

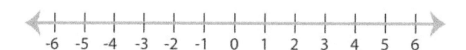

5) $x < -5$

6) $x > -2$

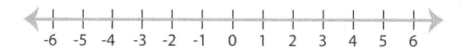

7) $x < 0$

8) $x < 4$

One–Step Inequalities

✎ **Solve each inequality and graph it.**

1) $x + 2 \geq 3$

2) $x - 1 \leq 2$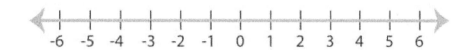

3) $2x \geq 12$

4) $4 + x \leq 5$

5) $x + 3 \leq -3$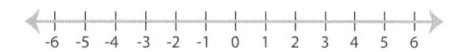

6) $4x \geq 16$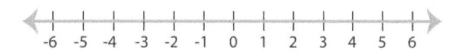

7) $9x \leq 18$

8) $x + 2 \geq 7$

Answers of Worksheets – Chapter 6

Equations

1) 10	11) 9	21) 24
2) 14	12) 14	22) -13
3) 3	13) 20	23) 45
4) 5	14) -21	24) -37
5) 3	15) -21	25) 30
6) 6	16) 4	26) 4
7) 11	17) -16	27) 50
8) 6	18) 20	28) 42
9) 19	19) 30	29) 33
10) -4	20) -9	30) 28

Graphing Inequalities

1)

2)

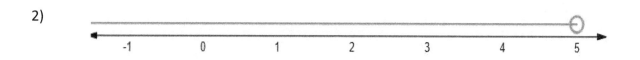

3)

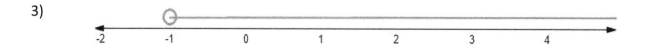

4)

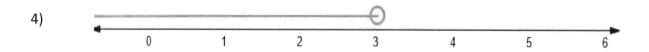

5)

6)

7)

8)

One-Step Inequalities

1)

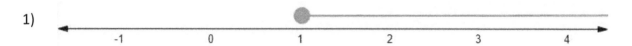

2)

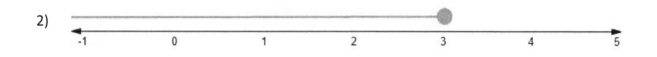

3)

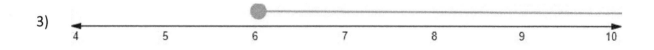

4)

5)

6)

7)

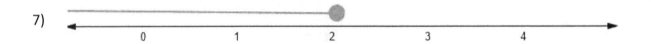

8)

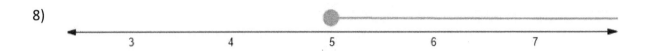

Chapter 7:

Exponents and Radicals

Topics that you'll practice in this chapter:

- ✓ Multiplication Property of Exponents
- ✓ Division Property of Exponents
- ✓ Powers of Products and Quotients
- ✓ Zero and Negative Exponents
- ✓ Negative Exponents and Negative Bases
- ✓ Writing Scientific Notation
- ✓ Square Roots

Mathematics is no more computation than typing is literature.

– John Allen Paulos

Multiplication Property of Exponents

✍ *Simplify and write the answers in exponential terms.*

1) $2 \times 2^2 =$

2) $5^3 \times 5 =$

3) $3^2 \times 3^2 =$

4) $4^2 \times 4^2 =$

5) $7^3 \times 7^2 \times 7 =$

6) $2 \times 2^2 \times 2^2 =$

7) $5^3 \times 5^2 \times 5 \times 5 =$

8) $2^6 \times 2^3 \times 2^5 =$

9) $5^7 \times 5^6 \times 5^8 =$

10) $(2^3)^3 =$

11) $2^{10} \times 2^6 =$

12) $10^3 \times 10^2 =$

13) $(7^4)^2 =$

14) $(7^2)^3 =$

15) $(6^8)^2 =$

16) $(2^{12})^2 =$

17) $4^{12} \times 4^7 =$

18) $(8^{13})^3 =$

19) $(9^8)^5 =$

20) $4^6 \times 4^5 \times 4 =$

21) $3^7 \times 3^3 \times 3^9 =$

22) $5^4 \times 5^{11} \times 5^8 =$

23) $(2^8)^4 \times 2^9 =$

24) $22^7 \times 22^9 \times 22^{11} =$

25) $(13^9)^7 \times 13^{11} =$

26) $(7^9)^9 \times (7^{11})^8 =$

27) $(3^6)^{10} \times (3^{12})^3 =$

28) $(8^9)^7 \times (8^5)^{10} =$

29) $(11^4)^{12} \times (11^8)^8 =$

30) $(9^3)^{14} \times (9^{12})^4 =$

31) $(9^9)^4 \times (9^8)^5 \times (9^6)^6 =$

32) $(4^5)^7 \times (4^3)^9 \times (4^5)^9 =$

Division Property of Exponents

✎ **Simplify.**

1) $\dfrac{2^2}{2^3} =$

2) $\dfrac{2^4}{2^2} =$

3) $\dfrac{5^5}{5} =$

4) $\dfrac{3}{3^5} =$

5) $\dfrac{4}{4^3} =$

6) $\dfrac{7^4}{7^3} =$

7) $\dfrac{6^5}{6^8} =$

8) $\dfrac{5^9}{5^7} =$

9) $\dfrac{3^{11}}{3^8} =$

10) $\dfrac{7^{13}}{7^{18}} =$

11) $\dfrac{8^{12}}{8^5} =$

12) $\dfrac{3^{16}}{3^{13}} =$

13) $\dfrac{5^{14}}{5^8} =$

14) $\dfrac{11^9}{11^{12}} =$

15) $\dfrac{8^{15}}{8^{19}} =$

16) $\dfrac{12^{14}}{12^9} =$

17) $\dfrac{9^7}{9^{19}} =$

18) $\dfrac{5^{22}}{5^{17}} =$

19) $\dfrac{8^{18}}{8^{12}} =$

20) $\dfrac{5^{13}}{5^{24}} =$

21) $\dfrac{3^3}{9} =$

22) $\dfrac{7^8}{7^3} =$

23) $\dfrac{8^6}{8^7} =$

24) $\dfrac{9^2}{9^3} =$

25) $\dfrac{5^4}{25} =$

26) $\dfrac{8^2}{2^4} =$

27) $\dfrac{4^3}{4^6} =$

28) $\dfrac{9^3}{9^8} =$

29) $\dfrac{25^2}{5^3} =$

30) $\dfrac{7^3}{49} =$

Powers of Products and Quotients

✎ *Simplify.*

1) $(2^2)^2 =$

2) $(2^2)^3 =$

3) $(3^3)^4 =$

4) $(4^4)^2 =$

5) $(6^5)^3 =$

6) $(9^6)^4 =$

7) $(4^9)^5 =$

8) $(8^6)^7 =$

9) $(7^4)^9 =$

10) $(3^8)^8 =$

11) $(8^6)^9 =$

12) $(9^7)^8 =$

13) $(2^{12})^2 =$

14) $(x^5)^2 =$

15) $(2^2 \times 3^4)^4 =$

16) $(3^4 \times 5^4)^3 =$

17) $(8^2 \times 3^2)^2 =$

18) $(5^4 \times 7^3)^4 =$

19) $(3^6 \times 6^8)^2 =$

20) $(7^3 \times 9)^3 =$

21) $(4^9 \times 5^6)^3 =$

22) $(2^{10} \times 6^3)^3 =$

23) $(4^3 \times 9^3)^2 =$

24) $(3^3 \times 8)^2 =$

25) $(5^{11} \times 9^3)^2 =$

26) $(3^7 \times 7^5)^2 =$

27) $(2^4 \times 5^6)^5 =$

28) $(9 \times 5^3)^2 =$

29) $(6^2 \times 3)^3 =$

30) $(6^2 \times 8^5)^2 =$

31) $(2^3 \times 5^2 \times 3^3)^2 =$

32) $(3^3 \times 5^3 \times 2^5)^3 =$

Zero and Negative Exponents

✎ *Evaluate the following expressions.*

1) $1^{-1} =$

2) $2^{-2} =$

3) $0^{15} =$

4) $1^{-1} =$

5) $8^{-1} =$

6) $8^{-2} =$

7) $2^{-4} =$

8) $10^{-2} =$

9) $9^{-1} =$

10) $3^{-2} =$

11) $7^{-2} =$

12) $2^{-4} =$

13) $6^{-2} =$

14) $5^{-3} =$

15) $22^{-1=}$

16) $4^{-2} =$

17) $5^{-2} =$

18) $35^{-1} =$

19) $4^{-3} =$

20) $6^{-3} =$

21) $3^{-4} =$

22) $5^{-2} =$

23) $2^{-3} =$

24) $3^{-3} =$

25) $7^{-3} =$

26) $6^{0} =$

27) $8^{-3} =$

28) $9^{-2} =$

29) $10^{-3} =$

30) $10^{-9} =$

31) $\left(\frac{1}{2}\right)^{-1} =$

32) $\left(\frac{1}{2}\right)^{-2} =$

33) $\left(\frac{1}{3}\right)^{-2} =$

34) $\left(\frac{2}{3}\right)^{-2} =$

35) $\left(\frac{1}{5}\right)^{-3} =$

36) $\left(\frac{3}{4}\right)^{-2} =$

37) $\left(\frac{2}{5}\right)^{-2} =$

38) $\left(\frac{1}{2}\right)^{-8} =$

39) $\left(\frac{2}{5}\right)^{-3} =$

40) $\left(\frac{3}{7}\right)^{-2} =$

41) $\left(\frac{5}{6}\right)^{-3} =$

42) $\left(\frac{4}{9}\right)^{-2} =$

Negative Exponents and Negative Bases

✎ *Simplify.*

1) $-6^{-1} =$

2) $-5^{-2} =$

3) $-2^{-4} =$

4) $-2^{-3} =$

5) $4^{-1} =$

6) $-5^{-3} =$

7) $-7^{-5} =$

8) $-(2^{-2})(9^{-3}) =$

9) $(3^{-4})(5^{-1}) =$

10) $(2^{-6})(7^{-7}) =$

11) $-(8^2)(5^{-3}) =$

12) $-\dfrac{1}{7^{-6}} =$

13) $-\dfrac{2}{5^{-4}} =$

14) $\left(-\dfrac{1}{3}\right)^{-2} =$

15) $\left(-\dfrac{3}{4}\right)^{-2} =$

16) $-\dfrac{1}{(5^{-7})(8^{-2})} =$

17) $-\dfrac{2}{7^{-4}} =$

18) $-\dfrac{3^{-3}}{2^{-2}} =$

19) $-\dfrac{5}{7^{-3}} =$

20) $\dfrac{3}{-5^{-4}} =$

21) $\dfrac{(2)(3)}{(2)^{-3}(3)^{-1}} =$

22) $-\dfrac{(5)^{-2}}{(9)^{-3}} =$

23) $\dfrac{(4)(7)^{-2}}{-(5)^{-2}} =$

24) $\left(\dfrac{5}{9}\right)^{-2} =$

25) $\left(-\dfrac{9}{(2)(5)}\right)^{-3} =$

Scientific Notation

✍ **Write each number in scientific notation.**

1) $0.113 =$

2) $0.02 =$

3) $2.5 =$

4) $20 =$

5) $60 =$

6) $0.004 =$

7) $78 =$

8) $1600 =$

9) $1450 =$

10) $91,000 =$

11) $2000000 =$

12) $0.0000006 =$

13) $354000 =$

14) $0.000325 =$

15) $0.00023 =$

16) $56000000 =$

17) $2000000 =$

18) $78000000 =$

19) $0.0000022 =$

20) $0.00012 =$

✍ **Write each number in standard notation.**

21) $3 \times 10^{-1} =$

22) $0.5 \times 10^{-1} =$

23) $12 \times 10^{2} =$

24) $0.2 \times 10^{-3} =$

25) $1.5 \times 10^{-2} =$

26) $4 \times 10^{3} =$

27) $9 \times 10^{5} =$

28) $112 \times 10^{2} =$

29) $3 \times 10^{-5} =$

30) $8.3 \times 10^{-5} =$

Square Roots

Find the value each square root.

1) $\sqrt{0} = \underline{\quad}$

2) $\sqrt{1} = \underline{\quad}$

3) $\sqrt{4} = \underline{\quad}$

4) $\sqrt{16} = \underline{\quad}$

5) $\sqrt{9} = \underline{\quad}$

6) $\sqrt{25} = \underline{\quad}$

7) $\sqrt{49} = \underline{\quad}$

8) $\sqrt{36} = \underline{\quad}$

9) $\sqrt{64} = \underline{\quad}$

10) $\sqrt{81} = \underline{\quad}$

11) $\sqrt{121} = \underline{\quad}$

12) $\sqrt{225} = \underline{\quad}$

13) $\sqrt{144} = \underline{\quad}$

14) $\sqrt{100} = \underline{\quad}$

15) $\sqrt{256} = \underline{\quad}$

16) $\sqrt{289} = \underline{\quad}$

17) $\sqrt{324} = \underline{\quad}$

18) $\sqrt{400} = \underline{\quad}$

19) $\sqrt{900} = \underline{\quad}$

20) $\sqrt{529} = \underline{\quad}$

21) $\sqrt{1,600} = \underline{\quad}$

22) $\sqrt{169} = \underline{\quad}$

23) $\sqrt{196} = \underline{\quad}$

24) $\sqrt{2,500} = \underline{\quad}$

✎ **Evaluate.**

25) $\sqrt{4} \times \sqrt{16} = \underline{\qquad}$

26) $\sqrt{25} \times \sqrt{64} = \underline{\qquad}$

27) $\sqrt{9} \times \sqrt{4} = \underline{\qquad}$

28) $\sqrt{64} \times \sqrt{36} = \underline{\qquad}$

29) $\sqrt{25} \times \sqrt{25} = \underline{\qquad}$

30) $\sqrt{16} \times \sqrt{81} = \underline{\qquad}$

31) $\sqrt{4} + \sqrt{4} = \underline{\qquad}$

32) $\sqrt{25} + \sqrt{49} = \underline{\qquad}$

33) $2 \times \sqrt{64} - \sqrt{100} = \underline{\qquad}$

34) $\sqrt{121} \times \sqrt{36} = \underline{\qquad}$

35) $8 \times \sqrt{9} \times \sqrt{144} = \underline{\qquad}$

36) $\sqrt{49} - \sqrt{16} = \underline{\qquad}$

Answers of Worksheets – Chapter 7

Multiplication Property of Exponents

1) 2^3
2) 5^4
3) 3^4
4) 4^4
5) 7^6
6) 2^5
7) 5^7
8) 2^{14}
9) 5^{21}
10) 2^9
11) 2^{16}

12) 10^5
13) 7^8
14) 7^6
15) 6^{16}
16) 2^{24}
17) 4^{19}
18) 8^{39}
19) 9^{40}
20) 4^{12}
21) 3^{19}
22) 5^{23}

23) 2^{41}
24) 22^{27}
25) 13^{74}
26) 7^{169}
27) 3^{96}
28) 8^{113}
29) 11^{112}
30) 9^{90}
31) 9^{112}
32) 4^{107}

Division Property of Exponents

1) $\frac{1}{2}$
2) 2^2
3) 5^4
4) $\frac{1}{3^4}$
5) $\frac{1}{4^2}$
6) 7
7) $\frac{1}{6^3}$
8) 5^2
9) 3^3
10) $\frac{1}{7^5}$

11) 8^7
12) 3^3
13) 5^6
14) $\frac{1}{11^3}$
15) $\frac{1}{8^4}$
16) 12^5
17) $\frac{1}{9^{12}}$
18) 5^5
19) 8^6
20) $\frac{1}{5^{11}}$

21) 3
22) 7^5
23) $\frac{1}{8}$
24) $\frac{1}{9}$
25) 5^2
26) 2^2
27) $\frac{1}{4^3}$
28) $\frac{1}{9^5}$
29) 5
30) 7

Powers of Products and Quotients

1) 2^4
2) 2^6
3) 3^{12}
4) 4^8
5) 6^{15}
6) 9^{24}
7) 4^{45}
8) 8^{42}
9) 7^{36}

10) 3^{64}
11) 8^{54}
12) 9^{56}
13) 2^{24}
14) x^{10}
15) $2^8 \times 3^{16}$
16) $3^{12} \times 5^{12}$
17) $8^4 \times 3^4$
18) $5^{16} \times 7^{12}$

19) $3^{12} \times 6^{16}$
20) $7^9 \times 9^3$
21) $4^{27} \times 5^{18}$
22) $2^{30} \times 6^9$
23) $4^6 \times 9^6$
24) $3^6 \times 8^2$
25) $5^{22} \times 9^6$
26) $3^{14} \times 7^{10}$
27) $2^{20} \times 5^{30}$

28) $9^2 \times 5^6$

30) $6^4 \times 8^{10}$

32) $3^9 \times 5^9 \times 2^{15}$

29) $6^6 \times 3^3$

31) $2^6 \times 5^4 \times 3^6$

Zero and Negative Exponents

1) 1

2) $\frac{1}{4}$

3) 0

4) 1

5) $\frac{1}{8}$

6) $\frac{1}{64}$

7) $\frac{1}{16}$

8) $\frac{1}{100}$

9) $\frac{1}{9}$

10) $\frac{1}{9}$

11) $\frac{1}{49}$

12) $\frac{1}{16}$

13) $\frac{1}{36}$

14) $\frac{1}{125}$

15) $\frac{1}{22}$

16) $\frac{1}{16}$

17) $\frac{1}{25}$

18) $\frac{1}{35}$

19) $\frac{1}{64}$

20) $\frac{1}{216}$

21) $\frac{1}{81}$

22) $\frac{1}{25}$

23) $\frac{1}{8}$

24) $\frac{1}{27}$

25) $\frac{1}{343}$

26) 1

27) $\frac{1}{512}$

28) $\frac{1}{81}$

29) $\frac{1}{1000}$

30) $\frac{1}{1000000000}$

31) 2

32) 4

33) 9

34) $\frac{9}{4}$

35) 125

36) $\frac{16}{9}$

37) $\frac{25}{4}$

38) 256

39) $\frac{125}{8}$

40) $\frac{49}{9}$

41) $\frac{216}{125}$

42) $\frac{81}{16}$

Negative Exponents and Negative Bases

1) $-\frac{1}{6}$

2) $-\frac{1}{25}$

3) $-\frac{1}{16}$

4) $-\frac{1}{2^3}$

5) $\frac{1}{4}$

6) $-\frac{1}{5^3}$

7) $-\frac{1}{7^5}$

8) $-\frac{1}{(2^5)(9^3)}$

9) $\frac{1}{(3^4)(5)}$

10) $\frac{1}{(2^6)(7^7)}$

11) $-\frac{8^2}{5^3}$

12) -7^6

13) $-(2)(5^4)$

14) 9

15) $\frac{16}{9}$

16) $-(5^7)(8^2)$

17) $-(2)(7^4)$

18) $-\frac{2^2}{3^3}$

19) $-(5)(7^3)$

20) $-(3)(5^4)$

21) $(2)^4(3)^2$

22) $-\frac{(9)^3}{(5)^2}$

23) $-\frac{(4)(5)^2}{(7)^2}$

24) $\frac{9^2}{5^2}$

25) $-\frac{(2)^3(5)^3}{(9)^3}$

Writing Scientific Notation

1) 1.13×10^{-1}
2) 2×10^{-2}
3) $2.5\ 10^0$
4) 2×10^1
5) 6×10^1
6) 4×10^{-3}
7) 7.8×10^1
8) 1.6×10^3
9) 1.45×10^3
10) 9.1×10^4

11) 2×10^6
12) 6×10^{-7}
13) 3.54×10^5
14) 3.25×10^{-4}
15) 2.3×10^{-4}
16) 5.6×10^7
17) 2×10^6
18) 7.8×10^7
19) 2.2×10^{-6}
20) 1.2×10^{-4}

21) 0.3
22) 0.05
23) 1200
24) 0.0003
25) 0.015
26) 4000
27) 900000
28) 11200
29) 0.00003
30) 0.000083

Square Roots

1) 0
2) 1
3) 2
4) 4
5) 3
6) 5
7) 7
8) 6
9) 8
10) 9
11) 11
12) 15

13) 12
14) 10
15) 16
16) 17
17) 18
18) 20
19) 30
20) 23
21) 40
22) 13
23) 14
24) 50

25) 8
26) 40
27) 6
28) 48
29) 25
30) 36
31) 4
32) 12
33) 6
34) 66
35) 288
36) 3

Chapter 8:

Measurements

Topics that you'll practice in this chapter:

- ✓ Convert Measurement Units
- ✓ Metric units
- ✓ Distance Measurement
- ✓ Weight Measurement

Convert Measurement Units

✎ **Convert to an appropriate measurement unit. (Round to the nearest Hundredths)**

1) 4 m = _____ cm

2) 50 cm = _____ m

3) 5 m = _____ cm

4) 3 feet = _____ inches

5) 5 feet = _____ cm

6) 2 feet = _____ inches

7) 1 inch = _____ cm

8) 4 feet = _____ inches

9) 8 inches = _____ foot

10) 10 feet = _____ m

11) 15 cm = _____ m

12) 5 inches = _____ cm

13) 10 inches = _____ m

14) 15 inches = _____ cm

15) 12 inches = _____ m

16) 8 feet = _____ inches

17) 25 cm = _____ inches

18) 11 inches = _____ cm

19) 1 m = _____ inches

20) 80 inches = _____ m

21) 200 cm = _____ m

22) 5 m = _____ cm

23) 12 feet = _____ inches

24) 10 yards = _____ inches

25) 16 feet = _____ inches

26) 48 inches = _____ Feet

27) 4 inches = _____ cm

28) 12.5 cm = _____ inches

29) 6 feet = _____ inches

30) 10 feet = _____ inches

31) 12 yards = _____ feet

32) 7 yards = _____ feet

Metric Units

✎ *Convert to an appropriate Metric unit.*

1) 1 cm = _____ mm

2) 1 m = _____ mm

3) 5 cm = _____ mm

4) 0.1 cm = _____ mm

5) 0.2 m = _____ cm

6) 10 mm = _____ cm

7) 50 mm = _____ m

8) 10 cm = _____ m

9) 100 mm = _____ cm

10) 0.05 m = _____ mm

11) 1 km = _____ m

12) 0.01 km = _____ m

13) 500 cm = _____ m

14) 0.50 km _____ m

15) 100 cm = _____ m

16) 80 cm = _____ mm

17) 4 mm = _____ cm

18) 0.6 m = _____ mm

19) 2 m = _____ cm

20) 0.03 km = _____ m

21) 3000 mm = _____ km

22) 5 cm = _____ m

23) 0.03 m = _____ cm

24) 1000 mm = _____ km

25) 600 mm = _____ m

26) 0.77 km = _____ mm

27) 0.08 km = _____ m

28) 0.30 m = _____ cm

29) 400 m = _____ km

30) 5000 cm = _____ km

31) 40 mm = _____ cm

32) 800 m = _____ km

Distance Measurement

✎ *Convert to the new units. (Round to the nearest Hundredths)*

1) 1 mi = _____ ft

2) 1 mi = _____ yd

3) 1 yd = _____ m

4) 2 yd = _____ ft

5) 2 mi = _____ yd

6) 3 mi = _____ m

7) 5 mi = _____ ft

8) 6 m = _____ ft

9) 4 mi = _____ m

10) 10 mi = _____ yd

11) 9 mi = _____ yd

12) 12 mi = _____ yd

13) 10 mi = _____ ft

14) 15 mi = _____ ft

15) 20 mi = _____ yd

16) 16 mi = _____ yd

17) 2 mi = _____ ft

18) 21 mi = _____ ft

19) 6 mi = _____ ft

20) 3 mi = _____ yd

21) 72 mi = _____ ft

22) 41 mi = _____ yd

23) 62 mi = _____ yd

24) 39 mi = _____ yd

25) 7 mi = _____ yd

26) 94 mi = _____ yd

27) 87 mi = _____ yd

28) 23 mi = _____ yd

29) 2 mi = _____ m

30) 5 mi = _____ m

31) 6 mi = _____ m

32) 3 mi = _____ m

Weight Measurement

✍ *Convert to grams.*

1) 1 kg = _____ g

2) 3 kg = _____ g

3) 5 kg = _____ g

4) 4 kg = _____ g

5) 0.01 kg = _____ g

6) 0.2 kg = _____ g

7) 0.04 kg = _____ g

8) 0.05 kg = _____ g

9) 0.5 kg = _____ g

10) 3.2 kg = _____ g

11) 8.2 kg = _____ g

12) 9.2 kg = _____ g

13) 35 kg = _____ g

14) 87 kg = _____ g

15) 45 kg = _____ g

16) 15 kg = _____ g

17) 0.32 kg = _____ g

18) 81 kg = _____ g

✍ *Convert to kilograms.*

19) 10,000 g = _____ kg

20) 20,000 g = _____ kg

21) 3,000 g = _____ kg

22) 100,000 g = _____ kg

23) 150,000 g = _____ kg

24) 120,000 g = _____ kg

25) 200,000 g = _____ kg

26) 30,000 g = _____ kg

27) 800,000 g = _____ kg

28) 20,000 g = _____ kg

29) 40,000 g = _____ kg

30) 500,000 g = _____ kg

Answers of Worksheets – Chapter 8

Convert Measurement Units

1) 4 m = 400 cm
2) 50 cm = 0.5 m
3) 5 m = 500 cm
4) 3 feet = 36 inches
5) 5 feet = 152.4 cm
6) 2 feet = 24 inches
7) 1 inch = 2.54 cm
8) 4 feet = 48 inches
9) 8 inches = 0.67 foot
10) 10 feet = 3.05 m
11) 15 cm = 0.15 m
12) 5 inches = 12.7 cm
13) 10 inches = 0.25 m
14) 15 inches = 38.1 cm
15) 12 inches = 0.3 m
16) 8 feet = 96 inches

17) 25 cm = 9.84 inches
18) 11 inch = 27.94 cm
19) 1 m = 39.37 inches
20) 80 inch = 2.03 m
21) 200 cm = 2 m
22) 5 m = 500 cm
23) 12 feet = 144 inches
24) 10 yards = 360 inches
25) 16 feet = 192 inches
26) 48 inches = 4 Feet
27) 4 inch = 10.16 cm
28) 12.5 cm = 4.92 inches
29) 6 feet = 72 inches
30) 10 feet = 120 inches
31) 12 yards = 36 feet
32) 7 yards = 21 feet

Metric Units

1) 1 cm = 10 mm
2) 1 m = 1000 mm
3) 5 cm = 50 mm
4) 0.1 cm = 1 mm
5) 0.2 m = 20 cm
6) 10 mm = 1 cm
7) 50 mm = 0.05 m
8) 10 cm = 0.10 m
9) 100 mm = 10 cm
10) 0.05 m = 50 mm
11) 1 km = 1,000 m
12) 0.01 km = 10 m
13) 500 cm = 5 m
14) 0.50 km = 500 m
15) 100 cm = 1 m
16) 80 cm = 800 mm

17) 4 mm = 0.4 cm
18) 0.6 m = 600 mm
19) 2 m = 200 cm
20) 0.03 km = 30 m
21) 3,000 mm = 0.003 km
22) 5 cm = 0.05 m
23) 0.03 m = 3 cm
24) 1,000 mm = 0.001 km
25) 600 mm = 0.6 m
26) 0.77 km = 770,000 mm
27) 0.08 km = 80 m
28) 0.30 m = 30 cm
29) 400 m = 0.4 km
30) 5,000 cm = 0.05 km
31) 40 mm = 4 cm
32) 800 m = 0.8 km

Distance Measurement

1) 1 mi = 5,280 ft
2) 1 mi = 1,760 yd
3) 1 yd = 0.91 m
4) 2 yd = 6 ft
5) 2 mi = 3,520 yd
6) 3 mi = 4,828 m
7) 5 mi = 26,400 ft
8) 6 m = 20 ft
9) 4 mi = 6,437 m
10) 10 mi = 17,600 yd
11) 9 mi = 15,840 yd
12) 12 mi = 21,120 yd
13) 10 mi = 52,800 ft
14) 15 mi = 79,200 ft
15) 20 mi = 35,200 yd
16) 16 mi = 28,160 yd

17) 2 mi = 10,560
18) 21 mi = 110,880 ft
19) 6 mi = 31,680 ft
20) 3 mi = 5,280 yd
21) 72 mi = 380,160 ft
22) 41 mi = 72,160 yd
23) 62 mi = 109,120 yd
24) 39 mi = 68,640 yd
25) 7 mi = 12,320 yd
26) 94 mi = 165,440 yd
27) 87 mi = 153,120 yd
28) 23 mi = 40,480 yd
29) 2 mi = 3,219 m
30) 5 mi = 8,047 m
31) 6 mi = 9,656 m
32) 3 mi = 4828 m

Weight Measurement

1) 1 kg = 1,000 g
2) 3 kg = 3,000 g
3) 5 kg = 5,000 g
4) 4 kg = 4,000 g
5) 0.01 kg = 10 g
6) 0.2 kg = 200 g
7) 0.04 kg = 40 g
8) 0.05 kg = 50 g
9) 0.5 kg = 500 g
10) 3.2 kg = 3,200 g
11) 8.2 kg = 8,200 g
12) 9.2 kg = 9,200 g
13) 35 kg = 35,000 g
14) 87 kg = 87,000 g
15) 45 kg = 45,000 g

16) 15 kg = 15,000 g
17) 0.32 kg = 320 g
18) 81 kg = 81,000 g
19) 10,000 g = 10 kg
20) 20,000 g = 20 kg
21) 3,000 g = 3 kg
22) 100,000 g = 100 kg
23) 150,000 g = 150 kg
24) 120,000 g = 120 kg
25) 200,000 g = 200 kg
26) 30,000 g = 30 kg
27) 800,000 g = 800 kg
28) 20,000 g = 20 kg
29) 40,000 g = 40 kg
30) 500,000 g = 500 kg

Chapter 9:

Geometry and Solid Figures

Topics that you'll practice in this chapter:

✓ Angles

✓ Triangles

✓ Polygons

✓ Trapezoids

✓ Circles

✓ Cubes

✓ Rectangular Prism

Mathematics is, as it were, a sensuous logic, and relates to philosophy as do the arts, music, and plastic art to poetry. — K, Shegel

Angles

✍ **What is the value of x in the following figures?**

1)

112° $x°$

2)

91° $x°$

3)

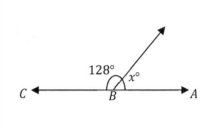

128° $x°$

4)

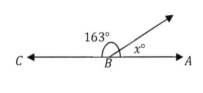

163° $x°$

5)

35° $x°$

6)

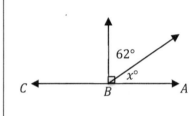

62° $x°$

✍ **Solve.**

7) Two complementary angles have equal measures. What is the measure of each angle?
_____

8) The measure of an angle is two third the measure of its supplement. What is the measure of the angle? _____

9) Two angles are complementary and the measure of one angle is 24 less than the other. What is the measure of the bigger angle? _____

10) Two angles are complementary. The measure of one angle is half the measure of the other. What is the measure of the smaller angle? _____

11) Two supplementary angles are given. The measure of one angle is 50° less than the measure of the other. What does the bigger angle measure? _____

Triangles

✍ *Find the measure of the unknown angle in each triangle.*

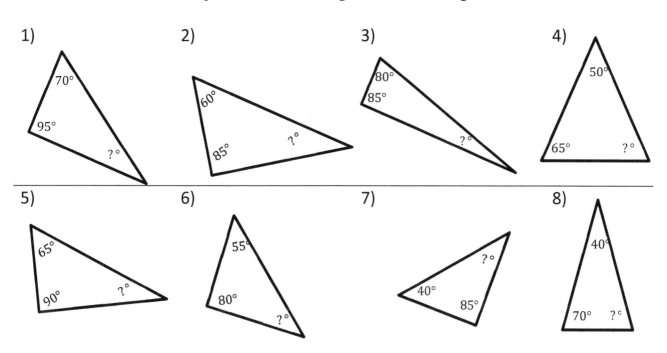

1) 70° 95° ?°

2) 60° 85° ?°

3) 80° 85° ?°

4) 50° 65° ?°

5) 65° 90° ?°

6) 55° 80° ?°

7) ?° 40° 85°

8) 40° 70° ?°

✍ *Find area of each triangle.*

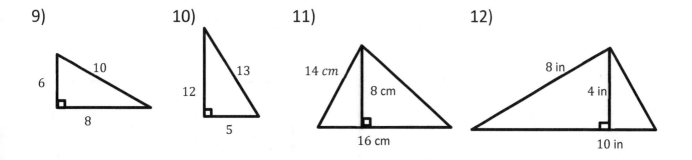

9) 6, 10, 8

10) 12, 13, 5

11) 14 cm, 8 cm, 16 cm

12) 8 in, 4 in, 10 in

Polygons

✍ **Find the perimeter of each shape.**

1)

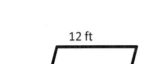

12 ft

12 ft   12 ft

12 ft

2)

10 in

8 in   8 in

10 in

3)

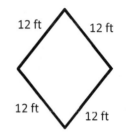

12 ft   12 ft

12 ft   12 ft

4) Square

14 cm

5) Regular hexagon

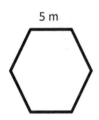

5 m

6)

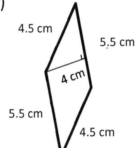

4.5 cm

5.5 cm

4 cm

5.5 cm

4.5 cm

7) Parallelogram

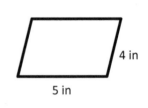

4 in

5 in

8) Square

6 m

✍ **Find the area of each shape.**

9) Parallelogram

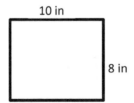

6 m

6 m

6 m

10) Rectangle

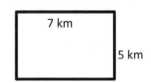

10 in

8 in

11) Rectangle

7 km

5 km

12) Square

7 in

Trapezoids

✎ **Find the area of each trapezoid.**

1)

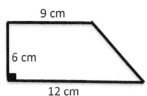

9 cm

6 cm

12 cm

2)

14 m

10 m

18 m

3)

5 ft

4 ft

7 ft

4)

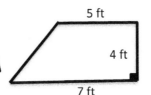

7 cm

5 cm

10 cm

5)

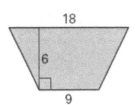

18

6

9

6)

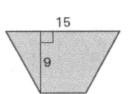

15

9

6

7)

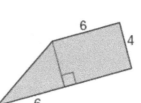

6

4

6

8)

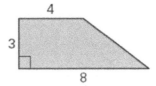

4

3

8

✎ **Solve.**

9) A trapezoid has an area of 60 cm² and its height is 6 cm and one base is 8 cm. What is the other base length? _____

10) If a trapezoid has an area of 65 ft² and the lengths of the bases are 12 ft and 14 ft, find the height. _____

11) If a trapezoid has an area of 180 m² and its height is 12 m and one base is 20 m, find the other base length. _____

12) The area of a trapezoid is 625 ft² and its height is 25 ft. If one base of the trapezoid is 15 ft, what is the other base length? _____

Circles

 Find the area of each circle. ($\pi = 3.14$)

1)   2)   3)   4)   5)   6)

7)   8)   9)   10)   11)   12)

 Complete the table below. ($\pi = 3.14$)

	Radius	Diameter	Circumference	Area
Circle 1	4 inches	8 inches	25.12 inches	50.24 square inches
Circle 2		12 meters		
Circle 3				12.56 square ft
Circle 4			18.84 miles	
Circle 5		5 kilometers		
Circle 6	6 centimeters			
Circle 7		8 feet		
Circle 8				28.26 square meters
Circle 9			43.96 inches	
Circle 10	5 feet			

Cubes

✍ **Find the volume of each cube.**

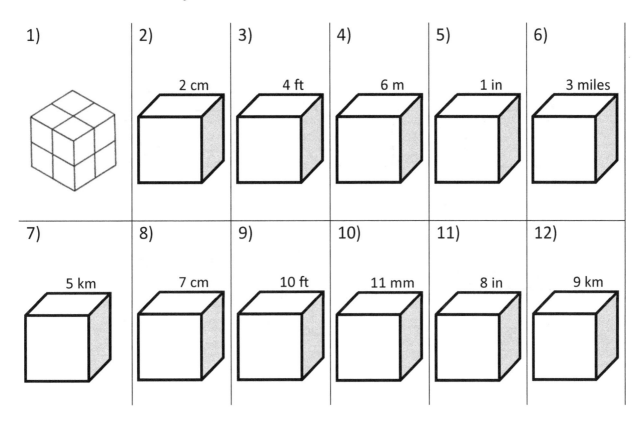

1)

2) 2 cm

3) 4 ft

4) 6 m

5) 1 in

6) 3 miles

7) 5 km

8) 7 cm

9) 10 ft

10) 11 mm

11) 8 in

12) 9 km

✍ **Find the surface area of each cube.**

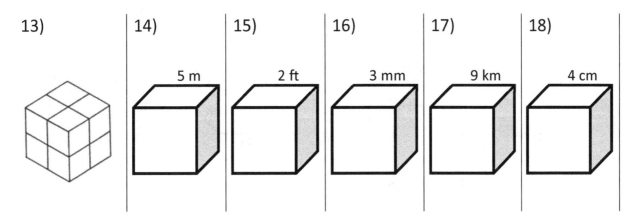

13)

14) 5 m

15) 2 ft

16) 3 mm

17) 9 km

18) 4 cm

Rectangular Prism

✍️ **Find the volume of each Rectangular Prism.**

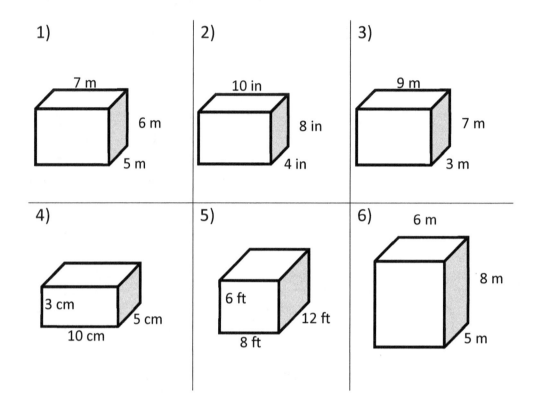

1) 7 m 6 m 5 m

2) 10 in 8 in 4 in

3) 9 m 7 m 3 m

4) 3 cm 5 cm 10 cm

5) 6 ft 12 ft 8 ft

6) 6 m 8 m 5 m

✍️ **Find the surface area of each Rectangular Prism.**

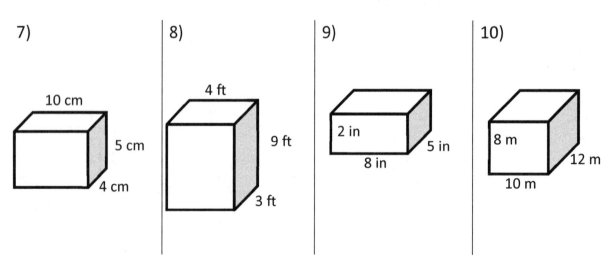

7) 10 cm 5 cm 4 cm

8) 4 ft 9 ft 3 ft

9) 2 in 8 in 5 in

10) 8 m 10 m 12 m

Answers of Worksheets – Chapter 9

Angles

1) 68°
2) 89°
3) 52°
4) 17°

5) 55°
6) 28°
7) 45°
8) 72°

9) 57°
10) 30°
11) 115°

Triangles

1) 15°
2) 35°
3) 15°
4) 65°

5) 25°
6) 45°
7) 55°
8) 70°

9) 24 *square unites*
10) 30 *square unites*
11) 64 *square unites*
12) 20 *square unites*

Polygons

1) 48 *ft*
2) 36 *in*
3) 48 *ft*
4) 56 *cm*
5) 30 *m*

6) 20 *cm*
7) 18 *in*
8) 24 *m*
9) 36 *m²*

10) 80 *in²*
11) 35 *km²*
12) 49 *in²*

Trapezoids

1) 63 *cm²*
2) 160 *m²*
3) 24 *ft²*
4) 42.5 *cm²*

5) 81
6) 94.5
7) 36
8) 18
9) 12 *cm*

10) 5 *ft*
11) 10 *m*
12) 35 *ft*

Circles

1) 50.24 *in²*
2) 113.04 *cm²*
3) 12.56 *ft²*
4) 314 *m²*

5) 28.26 *cm²*
6) 200.96 *miles²*
7) 12.56 *in²*
8) 3.14 *ft²*

9) 50.24 *m²*
10) 78.5 *cm²*
11) 113.04 *miles²*
12) 19.63 *ft²*

	Radius	Diameter	Circumference	Area
Circle 1	4 inches	8 inches	25.12 inches	50.24 square inches
Circle 2	6 meters	12 meters	37.68 meters	113.04 meters
Circle 3	2 square ft	4 square ft	12.56 square ft	12.56 square ft
Circle 4	3 miles	6 miles	18.84 miles	28.26 miles
Circle 5	2.5 kilometers	5 kilometers	15.7 kilometers	19.63 kilometers
Circle 6	6 centimeters	12 centimeters	37.68 centimeters	113.04 centimeters
Circle 7	4 feet	8 feet	25.12 feet	50.24 feet

Circle 8	3 square meters	6 square meters	18.84 square meters	28.26 square meters
Circle 9	7 inches	14 inches	43.96 inches	153.86 inches
Circle 10	5 feet	10 feet	31.4 feet	78.5 feet

Cubes

1) 8
2) $8\ cm^3$
3) $64\ ft^3$
4) $216\ m^3$
5) $1\ in^3$
6) $27\ miles^3$

7) $125\ km^3$
8) $343\ cm^3$
9) $1,000\ ft^3$
10) $1,331\ mm^3$
11) $512\ in^3$
12) $729\ km^3$

13) 24
14) $150\ m^2$
15) $24\ ft^2$
16) $54\ mm^2$
17) $486\ km^2$
18) $96\ cm^2$

Rectangular Prism

1) $210\ m^3$
2) $320\ in^3$
3) $189\ m^3$
4) $150\ cm^3$

5) $576\ ft^3$
6) $240\ m^3$
7) $220\ cm^2$
8) $150\ ft^2$

9) $132\ in^2$
10) $592\ m^2$

Chapter 10:

Statistics and Probability

Topics that you'll practice in this chapter:

- ✓ Mean and Median
- ✓ Mode and Range
- ✓ Histograms
- ✓ Stem–And–Leaf Plot
- ✓ Pie Graph
- ✓ Probability Problems

Mathematics is no more computation than typing is literature.

– John Allen Paulos

Mean and Median

✎ *Find Mean and Median of the Given Data.*

1) 3, 12, 5, 1, 8, 2

2) 3, 6, 3, 7, 4, 10

3) 14, 5, 1, 7, 9

4) 6, 4, 2, 8, 3, 2

5) 6, 5, 7, 5, 7, 1, 8

6) 6, 1, 4, 4, 9, 2, 9

7) 4, 1, 5, 9, 7, 7

8) 9, 5, 4, 9, 6, 7

9) 8, 5, 5, 6, 2, 4, 7

10) 10, 5, 2, 5, 4, 5, 8, 10

11) 15, 1, 5, 2, 2

12) 4, 3, 5, 9, 6, 14

✎ *Solve.*

13) In a javelin throw competition, five athletics score 56, 58, 63, 58 and 61 meters. What are their Mean and Median? _____

14) Eva went to shop and bought 3 apples, 5 peaches, 8 bananas, 1 pineapple and 3 melons. What are the Mean and Median of her purchase? _____

15) Bob has 12 black pen, 14 red pen, 15 green pens, 24 blue pens and 3 boxes of yellow pens. If the Mean and Median are 16 and 15 respectively, what is the number of yellow pens in each box? _____

Mode and Range

✎ **Find Mode and Rage of the Given Data.**

1) 8, 2, 5, 9, 1, 2

Mode: _____   Range: _____

2) 6, 6, 2, 3, 6, 3, 9, 12

Mode: _____   Range: _____

3) 4, 4, 3, 9, 7, 9, 4, 6, 4

Mode: _____   Range: _____

4) 12, 9, 2, 9, 3, 2, 9, 5

Mode: _____   Range: _____

5) 9, 5, 9, 5, 8, 9, 8

Mode: _____   Range: _____

6) 0, 1, 4, 10, 9, 2, 9, 1, 5, 1

Mode: _____   Range: _____

7) 6, 5, 6, 9, 7, 7, 5, 4, 3, 5

Mode: _____   Range: _____

8) 7, 5, 4, 9, 6, 7, 7, 5, 2

Mode: _____   Range: _____

9) 2, 5, 5, 6, 2, 4, 7, 6, 4, 9

Mode: _____   Range: _____

10) 7, 5, 2, 5, 4, 5, 8, 10

Mode: _____   Range: _____

11) 4, 1, 5, 2, 2, 12, 18, 2

Mode: _____   Range: _____

12) 6, 3, 5, 9, 6, 6, 3, 12

Mode: _____   Range: _____

✎ **Solve.**

13) A stationery sold 12 pencils, 36 red pens, 44 blue pens, 12 notebooks, 18 erasers, 34 rulers and 32 color pencils. What are the Mode and Range for the stationery sells?

Mode: _____   Range: _____

14) In an English test, eight students score 14, 13, 17, 11, 19, 20, 14 and 15. What are their Mode and Range? _____

15) What is the range of the first 6 even numbers greater than 11? _____

Histograms

✍ *Use the following Graph to complete the table.*

Day	Distance (km)
1	
2	

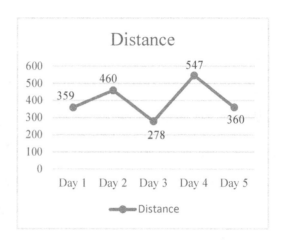

The following table shows the number of births in the US from 2007 to 2012 (in millions).

Year	Number of births (in millions)
2007	4.32
2008	4.25
2009	4.13
2010	4
2011	3.95
2012	3.95

Draw a histogram for the table.

Stem-And-Leaf Plot

Example:

56, 58, 42, 48, 66, 64, 53, 69, 45, 72

Stem	leaf
4	2 5 8
5	3 6 8
6	4 6 9
7	2

✎ *Make stem ad leaf plots for the given data.*

1) 74, 88, 97, 72, 79, 86, 95, 79, 83, 91

Stem | Leaf plot

2) 37, 48, 26, 33, 49, 26, 19, 26, 48

Stem | Leaf plot

Stem | Leaf plot

3) 58, 41, 42, 67, 54, 65, 65, 54, 69, 53

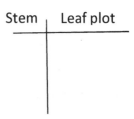

Pie Graph

The circle graph below shows all Jason's expenses for last month. Jason spent $300 on his foods last month.

Answer following questions based on the Pie graph.

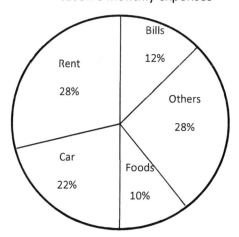

Jason's monthly expenses

1) How much did Jason spend on his car last month?

   _____

2) How much did Jason spend for foods last month?

   _____

3) How much did Jason spend on his rent last month?

   _____

4) What fraction is Jason's expenses for his bills and Car out of his total expenses last month? _____

5) How much was Jason's total expenses last month?

   _____

Probability Problems

✍ *Solve.*

1) A number is chosen at random from 1 to 10. Find the probability of selecting number 4 or smaller numbers. _____

2) Bag A contains 9 red marbles and 3 green marbles. Bag B contains 9 black marbles and 6 orange marbles. What is the probability of selecting a green marble at random from bag A? What is the probability of selecting a black marble at random from Bag B? _____ _____

3) A number is chosen at random from 1 to 50. What is the probability of selecting multiples of 10. _____

4) A card is chosen from a well-shuffled deck of 52 cards. What is the probability that the card will be a king OR a queen? _____

5) A number is chosen at random from 1 to 10. What is the probability of selecting a multiple of 3. _____

A spinner, numbered 1–8, is spun once. What is the probability of spinning ...

6) an EVEN number? _____   7) a multiple of 3? _____

8) a PRIME number? _____   9) number 9? _____

Answers of Worksheets – Chapter 10

Mean and Median

1) Mean: 5.16, Median: 4
2) Mean: 5.5, Median: 5
3) Mean: 7.2, Median: 7
4) Mean: 4.16, Median: 3.5
5) Mean: 5.57, Median: 6
6) Mean: 5, Median: 4

7) Mean: 5.5, Median: 6
8) Mean: 6.66, Median: 6.5
9) Mean: 5.28, Median: 5
10) Mean: 6.125, Median: 5
11) Mean: 5, Median: 2

12) Mean: 6.83, Median: 5.5
13) Mean: 59.2, Median: 58
14) Mean: 4, Median: 3
15) 5

Mode and Range

1) Mode: 2, Range: 8
2) Mode: 6, Range: 10
3) Mode: 4, Range: 6
4) Mode: 9, Range: 10
5) Mode: 9, Range: 4
6) Mode: 1, Range: 10

7) Mode: 5, Range: 6
8) Mode: 7, Range: 7
9) Mode: 2, 5, 6 and 4 , Range: 7
10) Mode: 5 , Range: 8
11) Mode: 2, Range: 17

12) Mode: 6, Range: 9
13) Mode: 12, Range: 32
14) Mode: 14, Range: 9
15) 10

Histograms

Day	Distance (km)
1	359
2	460
3	278
4	547
5	360

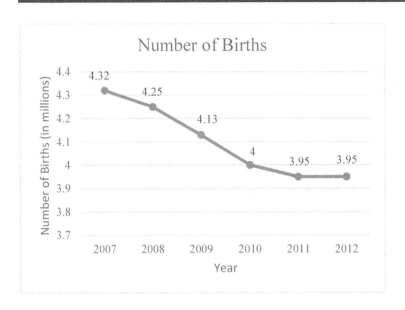

Stem–And–Leaf Plot

1)

Stem	leaf
7	2 4 9 9
8	3 6 8
9	1 5 7

2)

Stem	leaf
1	9
2	6 6 6
3	3 7
4	8 8 9

3)

Stem	leaf
4	1 2
5	3 4 4 8
6	5 5 7 9

Pie Graph

1) $550
2) $250
3) $700

4) $\frac{17}{50}$
5) $2500

Probability Problems

1) $\dfrac{2}{5}$

2) $\dfrac{1}{4}, \dfrac{3}{5}$

3) $\dfrac{1}{5}$

4) $\dfrac{2}{13}$

5) $\dfrac{3}{10}$

6) $\dfrac{1}{2}$

7) $\dfrac{1}{4}$

8) $\dfrac{1}{2}$

9) 0

STAAR Test Review

The State of Texas Assessments of Academic Readiness (STAAR) is developed under the supervision of the Texas Education Agency and is taken by all public school students in Texas, grades 3–12. The tests measure the progress of students from 3rd grade to 8th grade, as well as high school. STAAR is the state's testing program and is based on state curriculum standards in core subjects including:

- o Reading,
- o Writing,
- o Mathematics,
- o Science,
- o Social Studies

In high school, students take end-of-course STAAR exams in five high school subjects:

- o Algebra I,
- o Biology,
- o English I,
- o English II,
- o U.S. History.

Students take STAAR tests in the spring. The number of tests a student takes each year will depend on what grade he or she is in. Most students will have two to four testing days during a school year.

In this book, we have reviewed all mathematics topics being covered on the STAAR test for grade 6. In this section, there are two complete Grade 6 STAAR Math Tests. Take these tests to see what score you'll be able to receive on a real STAAR Math test.

Good luck!

STAAR Mathematics Practice Tests

Time to Test

Time to refine your skill with a practice examination

Take a practice STAAR Math Test for grade 6 to simulate the test day experience. After you've finished, evaluate your test using the answer key.

Before You Start

- You'll need a pencil and scratch papers to take the test.

- For each multiple-choice question, there are four possible answers. Choose which one is best. For grids in questions, write your answer in the box provided.

- It's okay to guess. You won't lose any points if you're wrong.

- After you've finished the test, review the answer key to see where you went wrong.

- **Calculators are NOT allowed for the STAAR Test Grade 6.**

Good Luck

STAAR Math Practice Test 1

State of Texas Assessments of Academic Readiness

Grade 6

Mathematics

2019

1) The ratio of boys to girls in a school is $5 : 7$. If there are 780 students in the school, how many boys are in the school?

A. 510

B. 480

C. 400

D. 325

2) Martin earns \$20 an hour. Which of the following inequalities represents the amount of time Martin needs to work per day to earn at least \$100 per day?

A. $20t \geq 100$

B. $20t \leq 100$

C. $20 + t \geq 100$

D. $20 + t \leq 100$

3) $(55 + 5) \div 12$ is equivalent to ...

A. $60 \div 3.4$

B. $\frac{55}{12} + 5$

C. $(2 \times 2 \times 3 \times 5) \div (3 \times 4)$

D. $(2 \times 2 \times 3 \times 5) \div 3 + 4$

4) What is the value of the expression $6(2x - 3y) + (3 - 2x)^2$, when $x = 2$ and $y = -1$?

A. -23

B. 41

C. 43

D. 49

5) Anita's trick–or–treat bag contains 14 pieces of chocolate, 15 suckers, 16 pieces of gum, 20 pieces of licorice. If she randomly pulls a piece of candy from her bag, what is the probability of her pulling out a piece of sucker?

A. $\dfrac{1}{13}$

B. $\dfrac{3}{13}$

C. $\dfrac{14}{65}$

D. $\dfrac{16}{65}$

6) In the following rectangle, which statement is false?

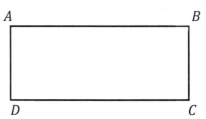

A. AD is parallel to BC

B. The measure of the sum of all the angles equals 360°.

C. Length of AB equal to length DC.

D. AB is perpendicular to AC.

7) The area of a rectangular yard is 80 square meters. What is its width if its length is 16 meters?

A. $9\ meters$

B. $7\ meters$

C. $5\ meters$

D. $3\ meters$

8) Which statement about 4 multiplied by $\frac{3}{5}$ must be true?

A. The product is between 1 and 2

B. The product is greater than 3

C. The product is equal to $\frac{75}{31}$

D. The product is between 2 and 2.5

9) Which of the following lists shows the fractions in order from least to greatest?

$$\frac{3}{4},\ \frac{2}{7},\ \frac{3}{8},\ \frac{5}{11}$$

A. $\frac{3}{8},\ \frac{2}{7},\ \frac{3}{4},\ \frac{5}{11}$

B. $\frac{2}{7},\ \frac{5}{11},\ \frac{3}{8},\ \frac{3}{4}$

C. $\frac{2}{7},\ \frac{3}{8},\ \frac{5}{11},\ \frac{3}{4}$

D. $\frac{3}{8},\ \frac{2}{7},\ \frac{5}{11},\ \frac{3}{4}$

10) A car costing $300 is discounted 10%. Which of the following expressions can be used to find the selling price of the car?

A. $(300)(0.4)$

B. $300 - (300 \times 0.1)$

C. $(300)(0.1)$

D. $300 - (300 \times 0.9)$

11) What is the missing price factor of number 420?

$$420 = 2^2 \times 3^1 \times \ldots$$

Write your answer in the box below.

12) If the area of the following trapezoid is equal to A, which equation represent x?

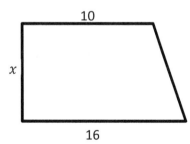

A. $x = \dfrac{13}{A}$

B. $x = \dfrac{A}{13}$

C. $x = A + 13$

D. $x = A - 13$

13) By what factor did the number below change from first to fourth number?

$$8, 104, 1352, 17576$$

A. 13

B. 96

C. 1456

D. 17568

14) 170 is equal to ...

A. $-20 - (3 \times 10) + (6 \times 40)$

B. $\left(\frac{15}{8} \times 72\right) + \left(\frac{125}{5}\right)$

C. $\left(\left(\frac{30}{4} + \frac{15}{2}\right) \times 8\right) - \frac{11}{2} + \frac{222}{4}$

D. $\frac{481}{6} + \frac{121}{3} + 50$

15) Round $\frac{215}{7}$ to the nearest tenth.

A. 31

B. 30.8

C. 30.7

D. 30

16) A chemical solution contains 6% alcohol. If there is 45 ml of alcohol, what is the volume of the solution?

A. 270 ml

B. 420 ml

C. 750 ml

D. 1,200 ml

17) Nicolas wrote an integer. The opposite of Nicolas's integer is -24. Which of the following statements about Nicolas's integer must be true?

   I.   The integer is -24.

   II.   The absolute value of the integer is -24.

   III.   The integer is 24.

   IV.   The absolute value of the integer is 24.

A. I and II

B. II and III

C. I and IV

D. III and IV

18) What is the volume of a box with the following dimensions?

Height $= 8\ cm$ Width $= 6\ cm$ Length $= 10\ cm$

A. $48\ cm^3$

B. $60\ cm^3$

C. $240\ cm^3$

D. $480\ cm^3$

19) The distance between two cities is $4,380\ feet$. What is the distance of the two cities in yards?

A. $1,460\ yd$

B. $11,406\ yd$

C. $48,618\ yd$

D. $52,920\ yd$

20) Mr. Jones saves $3,400 out of his monthly family income of $74,800. What fractional part of his income does Mr. Jones save?

A. $\frac{1}{22}$

B. $\frac{1}{11}$

C. $\frac{3}{25}$

D. $\frac{2}{15}$

21) What is the lowest common multiple of 18 and 28?

A. 252

B. 250

C. 245

D. 200

22) A bottle contains 48 fluid ounces of special chemical solutions. How many pints of chemical solution does the bottle contain?

A. $24\ pt$

B. $8\ pt$

C. $3\ pt$

D. $1.5\ pt$

23) $76\ kg = ...\ ?$

A. $76\ mg$

B. $7,600\ mg$

C. $760,000\ mg$

D. $76,000,000\ mg$

24) Calculate the approximate area of the following circle? (the diameter is 28)

A. 88

B. 615

C. 700

D. 2,462

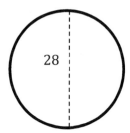

28

25) The following graph shows the mark of six students in mathematics. What is the mean (average) of the marks?

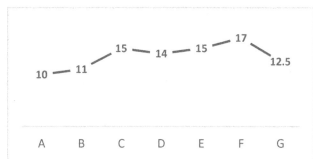

A. 13

B. 13.5

C. 14

D. 1.5

26) Which expression is equivalent to $5(12x - 16)$?

A. -20

B. $-20x$

C. $60x - 16$

D. $60x - 80$

27) Which ordered pair describes point A that is shown below?

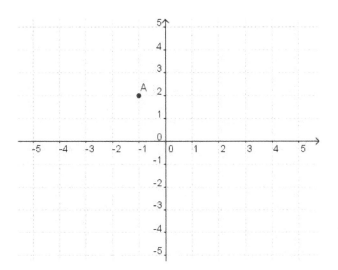

A. $(-1, 2)$

B. $(2, -1)$

C. $(1, -2)$

D. $(-2, 1)$

28) To produce a special concrete, for every $13\ kg$ of cement, $3\ liters$ of water is required. Which of the following ratios is the same as the ratio of cement to liters of water?

A. $91 : 21$

B. $14 : 4$

C. $39 : 6$

D. $9 : 39$

29) Find the opposite of the numbers 15, 0.

A. $\frac{1}{15}, 0$

B. $-15, 1$

C. $-15, 0$

D. $-\frac{1}{15}, 0$

30) What is the value of x in the following equation: $-60 = 115 - x$

A. 175

B. -175

C. 55

D. -55

31) Which of the following graphs represents the following inequality?

$$0 \leq x < 2$$

A.

B.

C.

D.

32) Which of the following statements is correct, according to the graph below?

A. The number of books sold in the April was twice the number of books sold in the July.

B. The number of books sold in the July was less than half the number of books sold in the May.

C. The number of books sold in the June was more than half the number of books sold in the April.

D. The number of books sold in the July was equal to the number of books sold in April plus the number of books sold in the June

33) What is the ratio between α and β $\left(\frac{\alpha}{\beta}\right)$ in the following shape?

A. $\frac{5}{14}$

B. $\frac{5}{13}$

C. $\frac{13}{5}$

D. $\frac{14}{5}$

34) A waiter earned a 19 percent tip. What decimal is equivalent to 19 percent?

Write your answer in the box below.

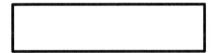

35) In a certain bookshelf of a library, there are 25 biology books, 110 history books, and 65 language books. What is the ratio of the number of biology books to the total number of books in this bookshelf?

A. $\frac{1}{4}$

B. $\frac{1}{8}$

C. $\frac{2}{7}$

D. $\frac{3}{8}$

36) Which of the following is the correct statement?

A. $\frac{3}{4} < 0.7$

B. $25\% = \frac{1}{2}$

C. $6 < \frac{11}{2}$

D. $\frac{4}{5} > 0.7$

37) Daniel is 66 years old, twice as old as Henry. How old is Henry?

A. 23 years' old

B. 25 years' old

C. 30 years' old

D. 33 years' old

38) An integer is chosen at random from 1 to 30. Find the probability of not selecting a composite number?

A. $\frac{13}{30}$

B. $\frac{6}{15}$

C. $\frac{11}{30}$

D. $\frac{1}{3}$

39) Which of the following statements can be used for the following inequality?

$$\frac{x}{8} \leq 16$$

A. Sara placed x pens among 16 friends and each friend received fewer than 8 pens.

B. Sara placed 8 pens among x friends and each friend received at most 16 pens.

C. Sara placed x pens among 8 friends and each friend received fewer than 16 pens.

D. Sara placed x pens among 8 friends and each friend received at most 16 pens

40) If the area of the following rectangular $ABCD$ is 140, and E is the midpoint of AB, what is the area of the shaded part?

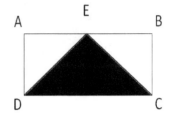

A. 100

B. 70

C. 50

D. 35

This is the End of Practice Test 1.   STOP

STAAR Math Practice Test 2

State of Texas Assessments of Academic Readiness

Grade 6

Mathematics

2019

1) Which of the following expressions has the greatest value?

A. $3^1 + 12$

B. $3^3 - 3^2$

C. $3^4 - 60$

D. $3^5 - 218$

2) The diameter of a circle is π. What is the area of the circle?

A. $2\pi^2$

B. π^2

C. $\dfrac{\pi^3}{3}$

D. $\dfrac{\pi^3}{4}$

3) Alfred has x apples. Alvin has 40 apples, which is 15 apples less than number of apples Alfred owns. If Baron has $\dfrac{1}{5}$ times as many apples as Alfred has. How many apples does Baron have?

A. 5

B. 11

C. 55

D. 275

4) In the following triangle find α.

A. 100°

B. 90°

C. 60°

D. 30°

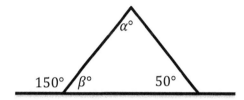

5) The price of a laptop is decreased by 25% to $525. What is its original price?

A. $340

B. $530

C. $700

D. $750

6) Find the perimeter of shape in the following figure? (all angles are right angles)

A. 21

B. 22

C. 24

D. 20

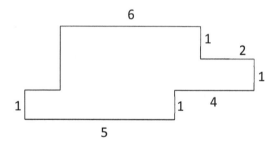

7) What is the probability of choosing a month starts with A in a year?

A. 1

B. $\dfrac{2}{3}$

C. $\dfrac{1}{2}$

D. $\dfrac{1}{6}$

8) What are the values of mode and median in the following set of numbers?

$$2, 4, 4, 7, 7, 6, 4, 2, 2, 1, 4$$

A. Mode: 2, Median: 2

B. Mode: 4, Median: 4

C. Mode: 3, Median: 2

D. Mode: 4, 3, Median: 4

9) Which expression equivalent to $x \times 92$?

A. $(x \times 90) + 2$

B. $x \times 9 \times 2$

C. $(x \times 90) + (x \times 2)$

D. $(x \times 90) + 2$

10) The ratio of pens to pencils in a box is 3 to 5. If there are 96 pens and pencils in the box altogether, how many more pens should be put in the box to make the ratio of pens to pencils $1 : 1$?

A. 22
B. 23
C. 24
D. 25

11) $4(1.052) - 3.126 = \cdots?$

A. 0.926
B. 1.082
C. 1.122
D. 1.134

12) Which list shows the integer numbers listed in order from least to greatest?

A. $-12, -4, -1, -2, 1, 3, 7$
B. $-12, -1, -2, -4, 1, 3, 7$
C. $-12, -4, -2, -1, 1, 3, 7$
D. $-1, -2, -4, -12, 1, 3, 7$

13) There are 44 blue marbles and 165 red marbles. We want to place these marbles in some boxes so that there is the same number of red marbles in each box and the same number of blue marbles in each of the boxes. How many boxes do we need?

A. 8

B. 9

C. 10

D. 11

14) What is the value of the following expression?

$$2,205 \div 315$$

A. 5

B. 6

C. 7

D. 8

15) Solve the following equation.

$$112 = 22 + x$$

A. $x = -90$

B. $x = 90$

C. $x = -134$

D. $x = 134$

16) Car A travels 221.5 km at a given time, while car B travels 1.2 times the distance car A travels at the same time. What is the distance car B travels during that time?

A. 222.7 km

B. 233.5 km

C. 241.5 km

D. 265.8 km

17) The perimeter of the trapezoid below is 38. What is its area?

A. 198 cm^2

B. 162 cm^2

C. 99 cm^2

D. 81 cm^2

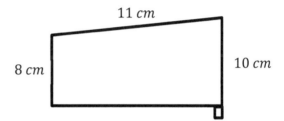

18) If point A placed at $-\dfrac{24}{3}$ on a number line, which of the following points has a distance equal to 5 from point A?

A. -13

B. -3

C. -2

D. A and B

19) Which of the following shows the numbers in increasing order?

A. $\frac{3}{13}, \frac{4}{11}, \frac{5}{14}, \frac{2}{5}$

B. $\frac{3}{13}, \frac{5}{14}, \frac{4}{11}, \frac{2}{5}$

C. $\frac{3}{13}, \frac{5}{14}, \frac{2}{5}, \frac{4}{11}$

D. $\frac{5}{14}, \frac{3}{13}, \frac{2}{5}, \frac{4}{11}$

20) What is the greatest common factor of 36 and 54?

A. 20

B. 19

C. 18

D. 17

21) Which expression is equivalent to $64 + 4 \cdot 16$?

A. $2^6 + 2^2 \cdot 2^4$

B. $2^5 + 2^2 \cdot 2^3$

C. $2^6 + 2^2 \cdot 2^3$

D. $2^5 + 2^2 \cdot 2^6$

22) A card is drawn at random from a standard 52–card deck, what is the probability that the card is of the soldier?

A. $\frac{1}{3}$

B. $\frac{1}{13}$

C. $\frac{1}{6}$

D. $\frac{1}{52}$

23) Which of the following statement can describe the following inequality correctly?

$$\frac{x}{5} \geq 9$$

A. David put x books in 5 shelves, and each shelf had at least 9 books.

B. David placed 5 books in x shelves so that each shelf had less than 9 books.

C. David put 9 books in x shelves and each shelf had exactly 5 books.

D. David put x books in 5 shelves, and each shelf had more than 9 books

24) Removing which of the following numbers will change the average of the numbers to 7.4?

$$1, 4, 5, 8, 11, 12$$

A. 4

B. 5

C. 8

D. 11

25) $20 \ mm \ = ...$?

A. $0.002 \ m$

B. $0.02 \ m$

C. $200 \ m$

D. $2000 \ m$

26) A football team won exactly 60% of the games it played during last session. Which of the following could be the total number of games the team played last season?

A. 63

B. 55

C. 48

D. 37

27) 8 less than twice a positive integer is 70. What is the integer?

A. 80

B. 78

C. 40

D. 39

Types of air pollutions in 10 cities of a country

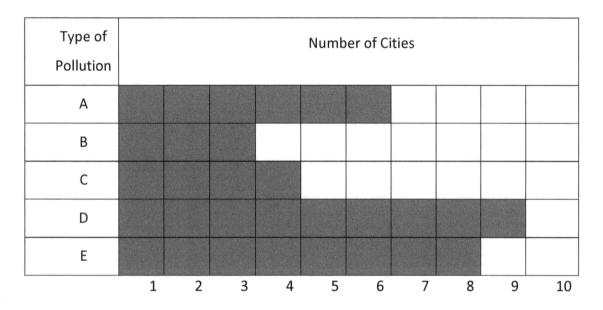

28) Based on the above data, what percent of cities are in the type of pollution A, C, and E respectively?

A. $60\%, 40\%, 90\%$

B. $30\%, 40\%, 90\%$

C. $30\%, 40\%, 60\%$

D. $40\%, 60\%, 90\%$

29) What is the missing term in the given sequence?

$$2, 7, 17, 37, 77, \underline{\quad}, 317$$

Write your answer in the box below.

30) If $4x - 1 = 9$, what is the value of $2x + 10$?

A. 30.5

B. 25

C. 20.5

D. 15

31) How many tiles of $9\ cm^2$ is needed to cover a floor of dimension $7\ cm$ by $36\ cm$?

A. 26

B. 27

C. 28

D. 29

32) If there are 400 students at a school and nearly 37% of them prefer to learn Germany, approximately how many students want to learn Germany?

A. 400

B. 252

C. 148

D. 130

33) A shaft rotates 360 times in 12 seconds. How many times does it rotate in 18 seconds?

A. 540

B. 450

C. 360

D. 100

34) If $x = -4$, which of the following equations is true?

A. $x(3x - 1) = 50$

B. $5(11 - x^2) = -25$

C. $3(-2x + 5) = 49$

D. $x(-5x - 19) = -3$

35) What is the missing prime factor of number 450?

$$450 = 2^1 \times 3^2 \times \dots$$

Write your answer in the box below?

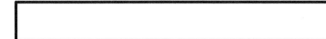

36) What is the area of the following triangle shape? (it's a right triangle)

A. $14 \ cm^2$

B. $24 \ cm^2$

C. $48 \ cm^2$

D. $80 \ cm^2$

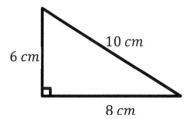

37) 65 is what percent of 50?

A. 50%

B. 77%

C. 130%

D. 140%

38) Which of the following expressions has a value of -23?

A. $-10 + (-8) + \frac{-5}{2} \times 2$

B. $5 \times 3 + (-2) \times 18$

C. $-10 + 6 \times 8 \div (-4)$

D. $(-3) \times (-7) + 2$

39) 300 inches equal to ...?

A. 3,600 $ft.$

B. 900 $ft.$

C. 100 $ft.$

D. 25 $ft.$

40) Which of the following equations is true?

A. $0.09 = \frac{9}{10}$

B. $\frac{20}{100} = 0.02$

C. $2.4 = \frac{24}{10}$

D. $\frac{35}{7} = 0.5$

This is the End of Practice Test 2.   STOP

STAAR Practice Tests

Answers and Explanations

STAAR Math Practice Test 1

1	D	21	A
2	A	22	C
3	C	23	D
4	C	24	B
5	B	25	B
6	D	26	D
7	C	27	A
8	D	28	A
9	C	29	C
10	B	30	A
11	7	31	B
12	B	32	C
13	A	33	B
14	C	34	0.19
15	C	35	B
16	C	36	D
17	D	37	D
18	D	38	C
19	A	39	D
20	A	40	B

STAAR Math Practice Test 2

1	D	21	A
2	D	22	B
3	B	23	A
4	A	24	A
5	C	25	B
6	C	26	B
7	D	27	D
8	B	28	A
9	C	29	157
10	C	30	D
11	B	31	C
12	C	32	C
13	D	33	A
14	C	34	B
15	B	35	5
16	D	36	B
17	D	37	C
18	D	38	A
19	B	39	D
20	C	40	C

STAAR Math Practice Test 1
Answers and Explanations

1) Choice D is correct

The ratio of boy to girls is $5 : 7$. Therefore, there are 5 boys out of 12 students. To find the answer, first divide the total number of students by 12, then multiply the result by 5.

$780 \div 12 = 65 \Rightarrow 65 \times 5 = 325$

2) Choice A is correct

For one hour he earns $20, then for t hours he earns $20t$. If he wants to earn at least $100, therefor, the number of working hours multiplied by 20 must be equal to 100 or more than 100.

$20t \geq 100$

3) Choice C is correct

$(55 + 5) \div (12) = (60) \div (12)$

The prime factorization of 60 is: $2 \times 2 \times 3 \times 5$

The prime factorization of 12 is: 3×4

Therefore: $(60) \div (12) = (2 \times 2 \times 3 \times 5) \div (3 \times 4)$

4) Choice C is correct

Plug in the value of x and y and use order of operations rule. $x = 2$ and $y = -1$

$6(2x - 3y) + (3 - 2x)^2 = 6(2(2) - 3(-1)) + (3 - 2(2))^2 = 6(4 + 3) + (-1)^2 =$

$$42 + 1 = 43$$

5) Choice B is correct

$\text{Probability} = \dfrac{number\ of\ desired\ outcomes}{number\ of\ total\ outcomes} = \dfrac{15}{14+15+16+20} = \dfrac{15}{65} = \dfrac{3}{13}$

6) Choice D is correct

In any rectangle, sides are not perpendicular to diagonals.

7) Choice C is correct

Let y be the width of the rectangle. Then; $16 \times y = 80 \rightarrow y = \dfrac{80}{16} = 5$

8) Choice D is correct

$$4 \times \frac{3}{5} = \frac{12}{5} = 2.4$$

A. $2.4 > 2$
B. $2.4 < 3$
C. $\frac{75}{31} = 2.419 \neq 2.4$
D. $2 < 2.4 < 2.5$ This is the answer!

9) Choice C is correct

Let's compare each fraction:

$$\frac{2}{7} < \frac{3}{8} < \frac{5}{11} < \frac{3}{4}$$

Only choice C provides the right order.

10) Choice B is correct

To find the discount, multiply the number $(100\% - \text{rate of discount})$

Therefore; $300(100\% - 10\%) = 300(1 - 0.1) = 300 - (300 \times 0.1)$

11) The answer is 7.

$$420 = 2^2 \times 3^1 \times 5^1 \times 7^1$$

12) Choice B is correct

The area of the trapezoid is: $area = \frac{(base\ 1 + base\ 2)}{2} \times height = \left(\frac{10+16}{2}\right)x = A \rightarrow$

$$13x = A \rightarrow x = \frac{A}{13}$$

13) Choice A is correct

$$\frac{104}{8} = 13, \frac{1352}{104} = 13, \frac{17576}{1352} = 13$$

Therefore, the factor is 13.

14) Choice C is correct

Simplify each option provided.

A. $-20 - (3 \times 10) + (6 \times 40) = -20 - 30 + 240 = 190$

B. $\left(\frac{15}{8} \times 72\right) + \left(\frac{125}{5}\right) = 135 + 25 = 160$

C. $\left(\left(\frac{30}{4} + \frac{15}{2}\right) \times 8\right) - \frac{11}{2} + \frac{222}{4} = \left(\left(\frac{30+30}{4}\right) \times 8\right) - \frac{11}{2} + \frac{111}{2} = \left(\left(\frac{30}{4}\right) \times 8\right) + \frac{111-}{2} =$

$(15 \times 8) + \frac{100}{2} = 120 + 50 = 170$ (this is the answer)

D. $\frac{481}{6} + \frac{121}{3} + 50 = \frac{481+242}{6} + 50 = 120.5 + 50 = 170.5$

15) Choice C is correct

$\frac{215}{7} \cong 30.71 \cong 30.7$

16) Choice C is correct

6% of the volume of the solution is alcohol. Let x be the volume of the solution.

Then: 6% of $x = 45\ ml \Rightarrow 0.06x = 45 \Rightarrow x = 45 \div 0.06 = 750$

17) Choice D is correct

The opposite of Nicolas's integer is -24. So, the integer is 24. The absolute value of 24 is also 24.

18) Choice D is correct

$Volume\ of\ a\ box = length \times width \times height = 8 \times 6 \times 10 = 480$

19) Choice A is correct

$1\ yard = 3\ feet$, Therefore, $4{,}380\ ft \times \frac{1\ yd}{3\ ft} = 1{,}460$ yd

20) Choice A is correct

3,400 out of 74,800 equals to $\frac{3{,}400}{74{,}800} = \frac{17}{374} = \frac{1}{22}$

21) Choice A is correct

Prime factorizing of $28 = 2 \times 2 \times 7$

Prime factorizing of $18 = 2 \times 3 \times 3$

LCM $= 2 \times 2 \times 3 \times 3 \times 7 = 252$

22) Choice C is correct

1 pt = 16 fluid ounces. Then: 16 fluid ounces = 3 pt

23) Choice D is correct

$1\ kg = 1000\ g$ and $1\ g = 1000\ mg$,

$76\ kg = 76 \times 1000\ g = 76 \times 1000 \times 1000 = 76{,}000{,}000\ mg$

24) Choice B is correct

The diameter of a circle is twice the radius. Radius of the circle is $\frac{28}{2} = 14$.

Area of a circle $= \pi r^2 = \pi(14)^2 = 196\pi = 196 \times 3.14 = 615.44 \cong 615$

25) Choice B is correct

$\text{Average (mean)} = \frac{\text{sum of terms}}{\text{number of terms}} = \frac{10+11+15+14+15+17+12.5}{7} = 13.5$

26) Choice D is correct

$5(12x - 16) = (5 \times 12x) - (5 \times 16) = (5 \times 12)x - (5 \times 16) = 60x - 80$

27) Choice A is correct

The coordinate plane has two axes. The vertical line is called the y-axis and the horizontal is called the x-axis. The points on the coordinate plane are address using the form (x, y). The point A is one unit on the left side of x-axis, therefore its x value is -1 and it is two units up, therefore its y axis is 2. The coordinate of the point isâ $(-1, 2)$

28) Choice A is correct

$91 : 21 = 13 : 3,$ $13 \times 7 = 91$ and $3 \times 7 = 21$

29) Choice C is correct

Opposite number of any number x is a number that if added to x, the result is 0. Thenâ

$15 + (-15) = 0$ and $0 + 0 = 0$

30) Choice A is correct

$-60 = 115 - x$

First, subtract 115 from both sides of the equation. Then:
$-60 - 115 = 115 - 115 - x \rightarrow -175 = -x$

Multiply both sides by (-1): $\rightarrow x = 175$

31) Choice B is correct

$-8 \leq 5x - 8 < 2 \rightarrow$ (add 8 all sides) $-8 + 8 \leq 5x - 8 + 8 < 2 + 8 \rightarrow 0 \leq 5x < 10$
$\rightarrow$ (divide all sides by 5) $0 \leq x < 2$

In inequality $0 \leq x < 2$, x is greater or equal to 0 and less than 2. Only choice B represent the same inequality on the number line.

32) Choice C is correct
A. Number of books sold in April is: 490
   Number of books sold in July is: $780 \rightarrow \frac{490}{780} = \frac{49}{78} \neq 2$
B. Number of books sold in July is: 780
   Half the number of books sold in May is: $\frac{1250}{2} = 625 \rightarrow 7800 > 625$

    C. Number of books sold in June is: 300

       Half the number of books sold in April is: $\frac{490}{2} = 245 \rightarrow 300 > 245$ (it's correct)

    D. $490 + 300 = 790 > 780$

33) Choice B is correct

α and β are supplementary angles. The sum of supplementary angles is 180 degrees.

$$\alpha + \beta = 180° \rightarrow \beta = 180° - \alpha = 180° - 50° = 130°$$

Then, $\frac{\alpha}{\beta} = \frac{50}{130} = \frac{5}{13}$

34) The answer is 0.19

19 percent = 0.19

35) Choice B is correct

Number of biology book: 25

Total number of books; $25 + 110 + 65 = 200$

The ratio of the number of biology books to the total number of books is: $\frac{25}{200} = \frac{1}{8}$

36) Choice D is correct

A. $\frac{3}{4} < 0.7$ $\frac{3}{4} = 0.75$. Therefore, this inequality is not correct.

B. $25\% = \frac{1}{2}$ $25\% = \frac{1}{4}$, not $\frac{1}{2}$.

C. $6 < \frac{11}{2}$ $\frac{11}{2} = 5.5$. Therefore, this inequality is not correct.

D. $\frac{4}{5} > 0.7$ $\frac{4}{5} = 0.8 \rightarrow 0.8 > 0.7$, this inequality is correct.

37) Choice D is correct

$$66 \div 2 = 33$$

38) Choice C is correct

There are 30 integers from 1 to 30. Set of numbers that are not composite between 1 and 30 is: $\{1, 2, 3, 5, 7, 11, 13, 17, 19, 23, 29\}$

11 integers are not composite. Probability of not selecting a composite number is:

$$\text{Probability} = \frac{number\ of\ desired\ outcomes}{number\ of\ total\ outcomes} = \frac{11}{30}$$

39) Choice D is correct

Let's write the inequality for each statement.

A. $\frac{x}{16} < 8$

B. $\frac{8}{x} \le 16$

C. $\frac{x}{8} < 16$

D. $\frac{x}{8} \le 16$ This is the inequality provided in the question.

40) Choice B is correct

Since, E is the midpoint of AB, then the area of all triangles DAE, DEF, CFE and CBE are equal. Total area of $ABCD$ is 140. So, the area of each triangle is $140 \div 4 = 35$

The area of the shaded part is: $2 \times 35 = 70$

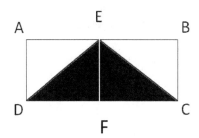

STAAR Math Practice Test 2
Answers and Explanations

1) **Choice D is correct**
   A. $3^1 + 12 = 3 + 12 = 15$
   B. $3^3 - 3^2 = 27 - 9 = 18$
   C. $3^4 - 60 = 81 - 60 = 21$
   D. $3^5 - 218 = 243 - 218 = 25$

2) **Choice D is correct**

   The radius of the circle is: $\frac{\pi}{2}$

   The area of circle: $\pi r^2 = \pi(\frac{\pi}{2})^2 = \pi \times \frac{\pi^2}{4} = \frac{\pi^3}{4}$

3) **Choice B is correct**

   Alfred has x apple which is 15 apples more than number of apples Alvin owns. Therefore:

   $x - 15 = 40 \rightarrow x = 40 + 15 = 55$

   Alfred has 55 apples. Then: $\frac{1}{5} \times 55 = 11$

4) **Choice A is correct**

   Supplementary angles add up to 180 degrees.

   $\beta + 150° = 180° \rightarrow \beta = 180° - 150° = 30°$

   The sum of all angles in a triangle is 180 degrees. Then:

   $\alpha + \beta + 50° = 180° \rightarrow \alpha + 30° + 50° = 180°$

   $\rightarrow \alpha + 80° = 180° \rightarrow \alpha = 180° - 80° = 100°$

5) **Choice C is correct**

   Let x be the original price.

   If the price of a laptop is decreased by 25% to \$525, then: $75\% \ of \ x = 525 \Rightarrow 0.75x = 525$
   $\Rightarrow x = 525 \div 0.75 = 700$

6) **Choice C is correct**

   Let x and y be two sides of the shape. Then:

   $x + 1 = 1 + 1 + 1 \rightarrow x = 2$

   $y + 6 + 2 = 5 + 4 \rightarrow y + 8 = 9 \rightarrow y = 1$

   Then, the perimeter is:

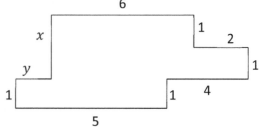

$1 + 5 + 1 + 4 + 1 + 2 + 1 + 6 + 2 + 1 = 24$

7) Choice D is correct

Two months, April and August, in 12 months start with A, then:

Probability $= \dfrac{number\ of\ desired\ outcomes}{number\ of\ total\ outcomes} = \dfrac{2}{12} = \dfrac{1}{6}$

8) Choice B is correct

First, put the numbers in order from least to greatest: $1, 2, 2, 2, 4, 4, 4, 4, 6, 7, 7$
The Mode of the set of numbers is: 4 (the most frequent numbers)

Median is: 4 (the number in the middle)

9) Choice C is correct

$x \times 92 = x \times (90 + 2) = (x \times 90) + (x \times 2)$

10) Choice C is correct

The ratio of pens to pencils is $3 : 5$. Therefore, there are 3 pens out of all 8 pens and pencils. To find the answer, first dived 96 by 8 then multiply the result by 3.

$96 \div 8 = 12 \rightarrow 12 \times 3 = 36$

There are 36 pens and 60 pencils $(96 - 36)$. Therefore, 24 more pens should be put in the box to make the ratio $1 : 1$

11) Choice B is correct

$4(1.052) - 3.126 = 4.208 - 3.126 = 1.082$

12) Choice C is correct

$-12 < -4 < -2 < -1 < 1 < 3 < 7,$ Then, choice C is correct.

13) Choice D is correct

First, we need to find the GCF (Greatest Common Factor) of 143 and 55.

$165 = 11 \times 15,\quad 44 = 4 \times 11 \rightarrow GFC = 11$

Therefore, we need 11 boxes.

14) Choice C is correct

$2{,}205 \div 315 = 7$

15) Choice B is correct

$112 = 22 + x,$ Subtract 22 from both sides of the equation. Then: $x = 112 - 22 = 90$

16) Choice D is correct

Distance that car B travels = $1.2 \times$ distance that car A travels = $1.2 \times 221.5 = 265.8$ Km

17) Choice D is correct

The perimeter of the trapezoid is 38.

Therefore, the missing side (height) is = $38 - 8 - 10 - 11 = 9$

Area of the trapezoid: $A = \frac{1}{2} h (b1 + b2) = \frac{1}{2} (9) (8 + 10) = 81$

18) Choice D is correct

If the value of point $A - \frac{24}{3} = -8$. A distance of 5 from Point A equals to: $-8 + 5 = -3$

Or $-8 - 5 = -13$

Choice D is correct.

A. $-\frac{24}{3} - (-13) = -8 + 13 = 5 = 5$
B. $-3 - \left(-\frac{24}{3}\right) = -3 + 8 = 5 = 5$
C. $-2 - \left(-\frac{24}{3}\right) = -2 + 8 = 6 \neq 5$

19) Choice B is correct

$\frac{3}{13} \cong 0.23$ $\qquad$ $\frac{5}{14} \cong 0.357$ $\qquad$ $\frac{4}{11} \cong 0.36$ $\qquad$ $\frac{2}{5} = 0.4$

Then: $\frac{3}{13} < \frac{5}{14} < \frac{4}{11} < \frac{2}{5}$

20) Choice C is correct

Prime factorizing of $36 = 2 \times 2 \times 3 \times 3$

Prime factorizing of $54 = 2 \times 3 \times 3 \times 3$

To find Greatest Common Factor, multiply the common factors of both numbers.

GCF= $2 \times 3 \times 3 = 18$

21) Choice A is correct

$$64 + 4 . 16 = 2^6 + 2^2 . 2^4$$

22) Choice B is correct

The probability of choosing a soldier is $\frac{4}{52} = \frac{1}{13}$

23) Choice A is correct

Let's write an inequality for each statement.

A. $\frac{x}{5} \geq 9$ (this is the same as the inequality provided)

B. $\frac{5}{x} < 9$

C. $\frac{9}{x} = 5$

D. $\frac{x}{5} > 9$

24) Choice A is correct

Check each choice provided:

A. 4 $\dfrac{1+5+8+11+}{5} = \dfrac{37}{5} = 7.4$

B. 5 $\dfrac{1+4+8+11+12}{5} = \dfrac{36}{5} = 7.2$

C. 8 $\dfrac{1+4+5+11}{5} = \dfrac{36}{5} = 6.6$

D. 11 $\dfrac{1+4+5+8+1}{5} = \dfrac{30}{5} = 6$

25) Choice B is correct

$1\,m = 1000\,mm$

$1\,mm = 0.001\,m$

Then, $20\,mm = 20 \times 0.001\,m = 0.02\,m$

26) Choice B is correct

Choices A, C and D are incorrect because 60% of each of the numbers is a non-whole number.

A. 63, $60\%\ of\ 63 = 0.60 \times 63 = 37.8$

B. 55, $60\%\ of\ 55 = 0.60 \times 55 = 33$

C. 48, $60\%\ of\ 48 = 0.60 \times 48 = 28.8$

D. 37, $60\%\ of\ 37 = 0.60 \times 37 = 22.2$

27) Choice D is correct

Let x be the integer. Then: $2x - 8 = 70$, Add 8 both sides: $2x = 78$

Divide both sides by 2: $x = 39$

28) Choice A is correct

Percent of cities in the type of pollution $A: \dfrac{6}{10} \times 100 = 60\%$

Percent of cities in the type of pollution $C: \dfrac{4}{10} \times 100 = 40\%$

Percent of cities in the type of pollution $E: \dfrac{9}{10} \times 100 = 90\%$

29) The answer is 157

Find the difference of each pairs of numbers: $2, 7, 17, 37, 77, \underline{\quad}, 317$

The difference of 2 and 7 is 5, 7 and 17 is 10, 17 and 37 is 20, 37 and 77 is 40, 77 and next number should be 80. The number is $77 + 80 = 157$

30) Choice D is correct

$4x - 1 = 9 \rightarrow 4x = 9 + 1 = 10 \rightarrow x = \frac{10}{4} = 2.5$

Then, $2x + 10 = 2(2.5) + 10 = 5 + 10 = 15$

31) Choice C is correct

The area of the floor is: $7\ cm \times 36\ cm = 252\ cm$

The number of tiles needed $252 \div 9 = 28$

32) Choice C is correct

Number of students prefer to learn Germany$= 37\%\ of\ 400 = \frac{37}{100} \times 400 = 148$

33) Choice A is correct

The shaft rotates 360 times in 12 seconds. Then, the number of rotates in 18 second equals to: $\frac{360 \times 18}{12} = 540$

34) Choice B is correct

Plugin the value of x in the equations. $x = -4$, then:

A. $x(3x - 1) = 50 \rightarrow -4(3(-4) - 1) = -4(-12 - 1) = -4(-13) = 52 \neq 50$

B. $5(11 - x^2) = -25 \rightarrow 5(11 - (-4)^2) = 5(11 - 16) = 5(-5) = -25$

C. $3(-2x + 5) = 49 \rightarrow 3(-2(-4) + 5) = 3(8 + 5) = 39 \neq 49$

D. $x(-5x - 19) = -3 \rightarrow -4(-5(-4) - 19) = -4(20 - 19) = -4 \neq -3$

35) The answer is 5.

Let x be the missing prime factor of 450.

$$450 = 2 \times 3 \times 3 \times x \Rightarrow x = \frac{450}{18} \Rightarrow x = 25 = 5 \times 5$$

The missing prime factor of 450 is 5.

36) Choice B is correct

$$The\ area\ of\ a\ triangle = \frac{1}{2}(base \times heigth) = \frac{1}{2}(6 \times 8) = \frac{1}{2}(48) = 24$$

37) Choice C is correct

Use percent formula: $Part = \frac{percent}{100} \times whole$

$65 = \frac{percent}{100} \times 50 \Rightarrow 65 = \frac{percent \times 50}{100} \Rightarrow 65 = \frac{percent \times 5}{10}$, multiply both sides by 10.

$650 = percent \times 5$, divide both sides by 5.

$130 = percent$,   The answer is 130%

38) Choice A is correct

Let's check the choices provided.

A. $-10 + (-8) + \frac{-5}{2} \times 2 \rightarrow -10 + (-8) + \frac{-5}{2} \times 2 = -10 + (-8) + (-5) = -10 - 13 = -23$

B. $5 \times 3 + (-2) \times 18 = 15 + (-38) = -21$

C. $-10 + 6 \times 8 \div (-4) = -10 + 48 \div (-4) = -10 - 12 = -22$

D. $(-3) \times (-7) + 2 = 21 + 2 = 23$

39) Choice D is correct

$1\ feet = 12\ inches.$ Then: $300\ in \times \frac{1\ ft}{12\ in} = \frac{300}{12}\ ft = 25\ ft$

40) Choice C is correct

A. $0.09 = \frac{9}{100}$

B. $\frac{20}{100} = \frac{2}{10} = 0.2$

C. $2.4 = 2\frac{4}{10} = \frac{24}{10}$

D. $\frac{35}{7} = 5$

www.EffortlessMath.com

... So Much More Online!

✓ FREE Math lessons

✓ More Math learning books!

✓ Mathematics Worksheets

✓ Online Math Tutors

Need a PDF version of this book?

Please visit www.EffortlessMath.com

CPSIA information can be obtained
at www.ICGtesting.com
Printed in the USA
LVHW060853110321
681214LV00011B/114

9 781970 036275